Testimonials

"Ruth is an outstanding individual and someone I would put great trust in regarding health. I've seen her for decades working through medical and then mental and social health systems and know that she approaches everything with care, thoughtfulness and insight that is of great benefit to all those she works with."

Peter J. McLean, CEO Chamber of Commerce and Community, Perth

"Ruth and I have facilitated groups in training and teaching. She shows good insight of the human condition, this being the emotional, physical, psychological and spiritual aspects of human beings."

Veronika Honner, Counsellor and University Lecturer, Perth

"Ruth Littler is continuously optimistic and supportive in all her interactions. She is reliable and adaptable to challenges."

Janette Morris, Education Consultant, Perth

"I have found Ruth to be genuine, compassionate about what she is doing through her work in therapy and mediation."

Siva Kumarasamy, Member of Pastoral Care Committee & Volunteer Animal Ethics Committee, Murdoch Children's Research Institute, Melbourne

"Ruth Littler has been coaching and supporting my professional transition, from a senior Registered Nurse to the Manager of Nursing Services to enable me to lead my team to achieve clinical governance and KPI goals."

***Sarah Attrill**, Perth*

"I have known Ruth Littler since 2018, we trained together at HeartMath Institute in Boulder Creek. We have shared experience and working relationships in promoting and applying resilience building techniques to the wider community in Australia, helping individuals and organisations flourish in optimising their wellbeing."

Teddy Craies, Wellbeing Coach, Trainer www.craieswellness.com

*"Ruth Littler has been an inspirational and valuable member of our Church Community. She has served in many roles including as a member of my Pastoral Team. Ruth sacrificed her time and shared her expertise by successfully facilitating multiple, "***Building Resilience Workshops***" for the community as a Church Outreach program."*

Peter Edalere, *Pastor, Grace Communion International, Western Australia.*

Live From the Inside Out

Heal and Reclaim Your Health

Ruth Littler

First published in Australia by OMNE Publishing in 2023

Text©2022 Ruth Littler

ALL RIGHTS RESERVED. No part of this book may be reproduced or transmitted in any form whatsoever, electronic, or mechanical, including photocopying, recording, or by any informational storage or retrieval system without the expressed written, dated and signed permission from the author.

A catalogue record for this book is available from the National Library of Australia

Author: Ruth Littler, RN, MSocSc, Grad Dip Human Services
Publisher: OMNE Publishing
Editor: Beth McBlain

LIMITS OF LIABILITY/DISCLAIMER OF WARRANTY: The author and publisher of this book have used their best efforts in preparing this material. The author and publisher disclaim any warranties (expressed or implied), or merchantability for any particular purpose. The author and publisher shall in no event be held liable for any loss or other damages, including, but not limited to special, incidental, consequential, or other damages. The information presented in this publication is compiled from sources believed to be accurate at the time of printing; however, the publisher assumes no responsibility for errors or omissions.

The information in this publication is not intended to replace or substitute professional medical advice. The author and publisher specifically disclaim any liability, loss, or risk that is incurred as a consequence, directly or indirectly of
the use and application of any of the contents of this information.

Dedicated to Alan, Chris and Sarah

Prosper and be in good health,
as your soul flourishes and thrives.

Acknowledgements

My deepest gratitude goes out to my late parents, Rachel Ivy and Joseph Egan. They were middle-aged when they migrated to Australia with four children. They endured tremendous hardship yet did their best for all of us. I am also immensely grateful for the support of my brothers, Roy (dec.) and Ashley and sister Patricia. They helped me persevere, have faith and be strong in spirit.

I appreciate my husband Alan, and young adult children Chris and Sarah. Their compassion, deep love, tolerance and feedback have helped me to grow, laugh at myself and lighten up. Thank you with all my heart.

Mohan Jayasekera and Dr. Bruce Wauchope (General Practitioner) helped me deeply to understand my union with God. Mike Popovich showed me how to manifest my new state of health and live abundantly through the creative power of God within me. I am eternally grateful to you all.

My sincere thanks to Beth McBlain, (Editor) and Andrew Akratos, (Book Cover and Interior Design) for the sparkle and zest you brought to the message in this book.

I am grateful to all the teachers featured in the book that include my clients, colleagues, friends and Health Professionals.

I thank God for giving me the courage to *'let myself out'* to write and publish this book.

What's Inside this Book?

Introduction

I describe how chronic disease robbed me of quality of life and the hoops I went through to heal. I show the *'Aha!' Moment* that brought about my health transformation. I moved from striving and feeling exhausted to being in awe and excited at what I learned researching epigenetics, new biology, resilience, spirituality and Biblical scriptures on my journey to reclaiming my health.

Chapter 1

I describe how self-healing occurs when you have Oneness with God. Historical and religious factors have hindered people's healing by promoting the idea that we are separated from God. The Mystery Union is introduced within these pages, showing there is no need for striving. When immersed in this Oneness, we rise up in power, with a knowing we are valuable, loved, delightful, victors, and then self-healing occurs.

Chapter 2

This chapter identifies the historical factors that have preserved the understanding in medicine; that the body and mind are separate entities.

This means symptoms are treated, and a holistic view of what is happening in the body is missed. We experience physical, mental and emotional stress symptoms because the integrated autonomic nervous system is activated. In chronic stress, the response becomes dysfunctional. When we believe our body, emotions, mind, and spirit work together, we will then have many options to maintain optimum health.

Chapter 3

The outer world is a reflection of our inner world. If the inner world is chaotic, it spills into all areas of life. Our inner world is everything inside us, our thoughts, feelings, beliefs, emotions, memories, values, and desires. When our inner world becomes calm, then the outer world follows. It's from the inner world we can create the future we want; the solution is inside.

The Outer World Follows the Inner World when we are calm, focused and flowing, we can respond appropriately to trauma and unexpected severe demands in this healing state.

Chapter 4

We can create a new state of health by thinking, believing and feeling like we already have the desired outcome.

Neuroscience educators will demonstrate how it works and how repeated visualisations of how we feel will rewire the brain and bring about significant biological changes

Chapter 5

Identifies or describes how our beliefs, thoughts and culture control our lives. I give examples to show how our beliefs run silently in the background. Limiting subconscious beliefs can keep us from taking opportunities or opening our mind to possibilities of healing, examples show that some people are sick because of secondary benefits. Whereas, beliefs of possibilities, also known as *Placebos*, can heal. Biology research shows that we can change our health and DNA with intentional positive thoughts about ourselves and the situations we face.

Chapter 6

Emotions can build or destroy health. Emotions are natural, whether negative, or positive. In this chapter, we see the body still reacts to feelings even if we do not express or repress emotions.

Dysfunction can occur when emotions are lodged in our bodies. Science and Spirituality findings will confirm how emotional upsets from our thoughts and attitudes cause disease. You will learn how depleting emotions can make us sick long-term and which emotions repair DNA. You will learn how to increase and replenish emotions.

Chapter 7

This chapter illustrates and describes how trauma is passed down through the generations. Starting to live with a new story helps us leave the past behind. You will be empowered to change the intensity of the emotion within sixty (60) seconds to access the healing state.

Chapter 8

Understand the principles to restore your body with 60- second strategies to boost energy. Believe you are resilient and that deep wells of strength are inside you. You will learn to identify the causes of energy depletion, energy leaks and danger signals of low oxygen and dehydration.

You will learn to move into a state of healing and sustain resilience.

Chapter 9

In this final chapter, I moved from frustration, anger and resentment when my message of spirituality and new scientific findings was not accepted favourably in my small Christian groups. I realised that blaming and holding resentment is like being in prison. *"It is like taking poison and expecting the other person to die!"*

However, the door is open, and we can let ourselves out anytime. I decided to move to a higher frequency or consciousness based on Dr. David R. Hawkins's *Map of Consciousness*. By moving to elevated emotions such as acceptance, no judgement, love and peace, we undo the many sources of suffering and increase the joy in our lives. I also find that *Let Yourself Out* means to step out, act on your vision and live your calling and your best life from the inside out.

The conclusion is to live your new story every day and co-create a new state of health.

Table of Contents

Preface

After 10 years of chronic illness, searching for answers and not being healed, I realised that *I focused on what I did not want instead of what I wanted.* This hindered healing. So, when I realised that I could imagine what being healthy was like and feel how great the feeling of having it already was, my energy shifted. I was able to co-create and manifest the health I wanted.

Understanding that the inside needed changing to bring calmness, peace and love to the outside helped me release the unexpressed emotions lodged in my organs. It became easier to change my thinking, shift painful emotions, and to reverse pathological processes. This allowed me to function effortlessly in many areas of my life.

This book will excite you as you uncover what caused your health problems in the first place, and you will learn how to undo them. You will discover changes in health occur when we believe and imagine that healing has already happened.

Remember the title of this book, Live From the Inside Out.

Definitions

Belief is "The feeling of being certain that something exists or is true." (Cambridge Dictionary)

Coherence is "The state when the heart, mind and emotions are in energetic alignment and cooperation. It is a state that builds resilience, personal energy is accumulated, not wasted, leaving more energy to manifest intentions and harmonious outcomes." (HeartMath Institute)

Elevated Emotions "Are qualities of the heart such as appreciation, courage, compassion, love, joy, kindness and courage. These emotions raise our vibrations." (Unlimited with Dr Joe Dispenza website)

Emotions are a "Combination of feeling sensations, associated mental thoughts, emotions and biochemical reactions, which shape our emotional experience, in gradations from very pleasant to very painful." (HeartMath Institute)

Epigenetics is "The study of how your behaviours and environment can cause changes that affect the way your genes work. Unlike genetic changes, epigenetic changes are reversible and do not change your DNA sequence, but they can change how your body reads a DNA sequence." (Centre for Disease Control)

Feelings can be defined as a person's response to the emotion that comes from the perception of a situation. (Mind Valley)

Heal comes from the Hebrew word *Rapha* which means to heal, to make healthful, to sew together, to mend, or repair. Heal comes from the Greek word *Sozo*, meaning to save, heal, or make whole.(Biblestudytools.com)

Neurons are "Cells that carry information throughout the body and co-ordinate all the functions of the body." (Medical News)

New Biology integrates biology with computer science, mathematicians and engineers to improve human health. (The 21st Century, National Academy.org)

Placebo is a substance given to someone who is told that it is a particular medicine, either to make that person feel as if they are getting better or to compare the effect of a particular medicine when given to others. (Cambridge Dictionary)

Resilience is "The ability to prepare for, recover from and adapt in the face of stress, adversity and challenge, is vital to your physical, mental, emotional and spiritual health." (HeartMath Institute)

Vitiligo (vit-ih-LIE-go) is a disease that causes loss of skin colour in patches. The discoloured areas occur on any part or large areas of the body which is more noticeable on darker skin. (Mayo Clinic)

Part 1

The Power Inside

Introduction

Aha! The moment that brought on My Transformation

"My people perish for the lack of knowledge."

I heard these words but did not expect this answer when I asked God why I was frequently sick?

I did not understand these words and forgot about them. This happened to me on September 30th, 2009. I was in a four-bed hospital ward feeling dreadful and being treated for a large abscess close to my jugular vein. I was discharged soon after and returned to work.

As the years went by, I found it hard to keep up with my work and felt stressed. I woke up daily feeling tired, weary, and inadequate, constantly being busy but not getting on top of things. I had widespread itchy and painful Psoriasis, Dermatitis, and Vitiligo. My hair fell out, and I had uncontrolled blood sugar levels. To say, I felt terrible and embarrassed would be a vast understatement.

It took a massive toll on me, resulting in burnout and being chronically ill for a very long time.

I went to Christian Healing meetings, where I witnessed many miracles. However, my health conditions did not improve or change. I went to different churches in Perth that offered prayers for healing, where a healing team would pray for each person.

I noticed very quickly the person praying for me would tell me that curses had to be broken off in my ancestry line. No one else around me asking for prayers was told that. One Prayer leader explained this was necessary due to my ethnicity. No one asked me if I ever had anyone pray to break off ancestry curses or about my long history of Anglo-Indian heritage, or the many generations of Christians in my family.

They never knew who I was.

I started to feel uneasy when I was interviewed privately. A Healing Facilitator asked questions to see what sin was lurking. I was expected to repent and renounce my ancestors and my sins whenever I was asked a question. I was also told to renounce the lies I believed because I was a member of a legalistic church for 20 years.

I used to assess Residential Aged Care Providers against Accreditation standards.

I smiled as I gave this Facilitator the *'right'* answers to tick the boxes so I could show them that I met the standards. However, my smile did not last long. I was told that God kept unclean people outside the camp in Ancient Israel who had sins like mine.

I was appalled! It triggered a deep pain inside me, feeling not being good enough, accepted or approved. Do you know what I mean?

The late Louise Hay, Author of **Heal Your Body A-Z**, said that the probable cause of Vitiligo is *"Feeling completely outside of things, not belonging, not one of the group."*[1] I had years of feeling rejected, not included, and as if I did not belong. It hurt so badly to think that even at this time, when I was desperate for healing; I was seen as not being good enough and not approved. I walked away and did not go back.

By 2017, the illness could not be hidden anymore. I had frequent infections, my work productivity dropped off, and I could no longer stand the bleeding and pain in my skin. I asked a Dermatologist what the cause was. He turned to the computer, printed an information sheet on stress management, and gave it to me. I got into my car and burst into tears.

I knew that stress caused skin disorders, but I did not know how to change things.

I hated feeling powerless. Looking at the medical bill in my hand, I decided, *"No more feeling powerless; I will take back my power. I will find how to reclaim my health."*

Even though my body was under severe strain, I was not treated holistically; only symptoms were treated by medical professionals working in separate or isolated silos. I spent thousands of dollars on investigations and treatments over the years. It was like a revolving door, and I was told to return if things did not improve, so I kept on returning over and over again for years.

Around this time, my husband and I went on a cruise in the South Pacific, where we attended an impromptu church service on board the ship. The speaker told us about a story of a man with leprosy who saw Jesus and said, *"Lord, if you are willing, you can make me clean."* Moved with compassion, Jesus said, *"I am willing,"* and the leprosy left. I was blown away! What! No repentance, No renouncing of sins or breaking curses or telling the man he must be outside the camp until he cleaned up.

Jesus touched the man even though it was forbidden for anyone with leprosy to get close to other people.

Wow! I was excited! I felt immense relief and exonerated because I felt convicted by the Healing Facilitator, who wanted me to clean up before letting God heal me.

For the first time in my life, I saw firsthand how cultural, historical and religious factors hindered healing. Instead, I experienced Jesus as compassionate who was willing to heal and no cleaning up before was needed.

Soon after this experience, I sat in my church listening to a guest speaker, Dr. Bruce Wauhope, a General Practitioner; the topic was the: **Mystery Union** (Christ in us). His glasses were perched on his nose. Looking at me, he spoke loudly, *"Christ is in you, and you are whole."*

In a flash, I saw myself in the hospital ward hearing, *"My people perish for the lack of knowledge."* I was already in union with God. I had everything I needed, all resources. I was accepted, greatly loved and embraced, even the parts inside me that I hated and kept hidden. I am never separated from God.

I was in awe, astonished and teary. Aha! This was the knowledge I lacked.

I wanted to understand more about what *perish for* the lack of knowledge meant, so I searched till I found Matthew McDonald's blog in: **Thought for Today** to illustrate, *"My People Perish for the Lack of Knowledge."*[2]

A man in the early 1900s purchased his ticket and went on a cruise from England to America. However, he stayed in his cabin every night during dinner. Because he thought his ticket did not include food, he brought his own food with him to last the journey. On the last day of the cruise, the Captain asked, *"Why had he never seen him at meal times?"*

The man explained his reason. The Captain replied, *"Sir, the ticket included every meal as well."*

Reading this story opened up a dam of tears in me. I lacked knowledge. **I had God in me.** I had every resource and was loved and approved of, yet my religious teaching since Sunday school has been, "*Do more, keep striving,*" to be accepted by God. It was about being moralistic, looking good, judging and excluding others from the church who didn't match up or fit in.

I did not hear I was good enough. Instead, I heard from the pulpit, *"We are like filthy rags."* I worked hard to do it right.

I was petrified of being left back from a story I heard as a child, *'Be ready for Jesus's return or else you'll be left back.'* This pain of striving unconsciously impacted me in all areas of life, including how I parented my children. No wonder I was sick and exhausted; I cried, for myself and my family at what we had lost.

We were perishing for the lack of knowledge. Perishing also means dying, losing quality, decay, rot and suffering.

I see so many people suffering as I did because of not feeling loved and accepted unconditionally. They hide to avoid rejection or disapproval. They do not step out or up because of the pain of not feeling good enough or guilt or shame. When we hide, the cost is exceptionally high as we can never become all we can be.

This is what mobilised me. I learned how shame, guilt, unexpressed emotions and limiting beliefs, thoughts, traditions and cultures can deplete energy and prevent the genes from expressing themselves for optimum health.

Did you know that a DNA molecule unwinds itself when it's in an environment of love?

Feeling loved and accepted increases energy, rewires the brain, and repairs and restores the body.

I decided to find out all I could about healing and reclaiming my health. This led me to carefully look at Biblical scriptures and research in Epigenetics, Nutrition, New Biology, Resilience and Stress Transformation. I implemented everything I learned, increased my vitality and set out to reclaim my health.

Why this book? Live From the Inside Out

I wrote this book to explain from my experience and my personal point of view that people who are chronically ill, do not have to jump through hoops to be healed. Everyone is unique, and there are many different modes of healing.

My intention is to provide information that can help you create a new state of health. You will be excited as you discover how our body continually heals, restores itself and repairs continuously.

This book has three parts. The first part describes the foundation to recognise and acknowledge the power inside you, then to undo the health problem.

The second part shows how the lights on our genes get turned off or suppressed, causing the problem and how to express them or turn them back on for optimum health.

The third part is about giving yourself permission and allowing ourselves to live freely and feel fantastic, inside and out.

You will see that there is a personal and loving Creator that has left us a guide to keep the lights on in our genes and live freely and fully.

"It's not about finding the answers, but by undoing the basis of the problem."[3]

David R. Hawkins M. D, Psychiatrist and Spiritual Teacher

Chapter One

Living in the Mystery Union

Gregg Braden, in his book **Human by Design**, *from Evolution By Chance to Transformation by Choice*, says: *"We are the result of an intentional act of creation capable of empathy, compassion, love and self-healing."*[4]

Mathematical studies show the beginning of the Universe did not come about by a Big Bang. There is law and order, not chaos, in the cosmos. There is a higher knowledge of all the natural geometrical shapes around us, from the orbits of planets and raindrops to the hexagonal-shaped honeycombs.

"There is an intelligent order and sequence that governs every movement of this cosmos. Every atom of my body and every cell is programmed to move in accordance with a set of instructions which are flawless and harmonious in their programming." [5]

Peter Sage, Personal Transformation Expert

Dr. Joe Dispenza, an Educator and Researcher of Neuroscience, facilitates weeklong workshops where Stage 4 cancers and numerous debilitating diseases are known to disappear within four days.

Dr. Dispenza supports participants through meditation, to learn to surrender and become one with the **Infinite Intelligence Source.**

The goal is to create healing and generate a new state of health.[6]

Holistic healers from numerous different religions or spiritual beliefs agree that: *Oneness with a Divine becomes the unifying force to bring harmony to the body, mind and spirit, resulting in self-healing.*

This Divine Being is sometimes called Creator, Father, God, Higher Power, Infinite Intelligence, Infinite Source, Universe Life Force, or Supreme Being. However, one thing that seems to be missing is that God is not always seen as personal. Even Max Planck the Father of Quantum Mechanics, believed there was a Divine intelligent source.[7] Still, he did not believe in a personal God.

"What I mean is that a personal God is relatable, and enjoys having an intimate relationship with us."

Some of my clients have said, *"They could not relate to God as so many atrocities of child sexual, emotional and physical abuse occurred in religious organisaitons."*

Some clients were raised in the Christian faith but refuse to have anything to do with any church. They said, *"God is demanding, no fun, and who wants us to stop having any pleasure."*

A few Christian clients who had relatives seriously injured in natural disasters or have debilitating diseases said, *"God has punished them or their relatives."* One person said, *"God gave me cancer after I was furious and swore at him."* Another woman burdened with guilt told me that, *"Her child was born with Cerebral Palsy because God punished her for being unfaithful to her husband."*

A woman friend of mine told me someone came to her in a shopping mall and asked, *"Where would you go if you died tonight?" Then she was told that if 'she accepted Jesus, she would go to heaven; if not, she would go to hell.'* So, my friend *'accepted'* Jesus out of fear. Another woman told me, *"I am not into religion, but I am into love."*

Why are many of us missing this **Oneness with God** that Holistic healers and educators of neuroscience say brings healing? Have you ever wondered why God got such an awful reputation? Why is God not seen as personal? Does it even matter? Where did it come from?

According to religious journals, Plato's 428 -347BC philosophy of people being separate from God was integrated into Christianity in the 4th century. God could not be with matter (people). He was so pure that people had to live moral lives and become perfect to get to God.[8]

In addition, a sermon, **Sinners in the Hands of an Angry God**, was preached by Jonathon Edwards in 1741. This sermon describes, *'Black clouds of God's wrath directly over the heads of sinners, and if the dreadful storm is released, it will come with fury and destruction.'* People were told, "*The floods of God's vengeance have been withheld, but your guilt constantly increases, storing more wraths in God.*"

People were also told that, *"The sinner hangs by a slender thread in the hand of God whose anger is provoked and incensed against you unless you turn to him."*[9]

Jonathon Edwards's passion and love for God shines through in the book and there were large revivals in the eighteenth century based on his teaching.

However, as a child I often heard the message of God's fury since Sunday school and there was an expectation to keep striving, to be moralistic, and do more until I could be accepted by God or face destruction and separation forever.

I heard sermons years later when I was much older with these scriptures:

> *Christ holds everything together.*
>
> *Colossians 1.17*
>
> *Christ is in you. He is your hope of glory.*
>
> Colossians 1.27
>
> *You are one with me, for I will be living in you.*
>
> *John 14.20*

Yet our union with God known as the **Mystery Union** did not appear as significant to me as those teachings that focused on reconfirming my fear of fury, destruction and separation from God.

Since the fourth century, the doctrine of separation from God and having to clean up to get to Him for acceptance has been part of some Western Church's teachings and thinking for a long time.[10]

When we see God as personal and not punitive, full of light and love, we start welcoming new beliefs of how God sees and thinks of us.

In his book, **God Is For Us**, Baxter Kruger says, "*We are in union, everything God is already ours, joy, beauty and unbridled life, now, not in the future, so we can be filled to overflowing with the Divine love.*"[11]

Why does it matter to see God as loving?

Relationships embedded in fear do not increase intimacy. Fear stunts growth and keeps us in survival mode, where the lights of our genes get turned off. We stay as shadows; we are never fully present or authentic.

Threatening interactions are stressful. The stress response will be unconsciously and automatically activated and can result in increased heart rate, raised blood pressure, and aches and pains.

Imagine if we focused on living in this union known as the **Mystery Union.**

"***It means that the love and creative power of God is within us to change our circumstances and heal us.***"

We would be able to face any situation: illness, a life- threatening or debilitating medical diagnosis, traumatic events, death of a loved one, unemployment, desperate financial issues, or any traumatic event.

If we were living in the Mystery Union, we would stop losing sleep about whether we are doing the right thing and stop worrying and feeling guilty about going outside God's will.

What a different point of view we would be coming from.

Suppose we live from this understanding of **Oneness,** as we are already living in union with God. Our lives would change completely and instantly. Our perception of any problem we face would improve immediately.

God has embraced even the dark parts in us that private shadow self that we don't want anyone to know about.

Suffering comes from the perception that no one is there to help and provide for us.

Being aware of and acknowledging our **Oneness with God** calms us, nurtures us, and soothes us like when a newborn baby is comforted and held.

We become connected to everyone, and we have our being in Him. We are one with God and yet still distinct; we get to share in everything and all that He is.

When we have positive, peaceful and loving interactions, the perception of pain is decreased as the brakes are put on the stress response. People bloom in nurturing relationships.

The emotion of love signals new genes, rewires the brain, and strengthens the body's immunity. In the book, **The God-Shaped Brain**, *How Changing Your View of God Transforms Your Life*, by Dr. Timothy Jennings says *"Monks who meditated on a God of love had positive brain changes".*

Growth occurs in the brain's frontal cortex that is responsible for thinking, making judgements, expressing empathy, compassion, sharp thinking and memory.' Dr. Jennings cited this research from the University of Pennsylvania. They also found *telomeres* at the tips of chromosomes that protect DNA lengthen.

Meditation on a punitive, authoritarian critical and distant God resulted in fewer circuits' activated and chronic inflammation. Fear circuits grew stronger when anticipating the return of a punishing God, and the prefrontal cortex was damaged.[12]

I would like to invite you to:

1. Consider research from The University of Pennsylvania that showed meditating on a **God of Love** for 12 minutes a day results in positive changes in the brain and telomeres.

   You can replicate these results in your own meditation on a **God that is Loving.**

2. *Start undoing the effects of ill health and disease caused by feeling separated, rejected, not accepted or never ever good enough. Here are some scriptures about how God sees you. Your energy and good feelings will increase.*

"You are the pearl that takes God's breath away."

Matthew 13: 45-46

"You are a shining light."

I Thessalonians 5. 5

"You are the apple of God's eye."

Psalm 17.8

"You are God's great delight."

Psalm 18.19

Chapter 2

Unity of Body, Emotions, Mind, and Spirit

Have you ever felt as if you are not seen as a whole person? Health Professionals say they are providing holistic care. What is holistic care? Do you know? Did any of these health professionals ever think to review the physical, emotional, mental and social conditions around my life? Was the idea of integrating all my health conditions ever really recognised, reviewed and taken into consideration?

During my treatment over the years, it appeared to me that only my symptoms were being treated in different parts of my body by various specialists. Even though my body screamed in pain, my symptoms were treated by different doctors working in very separate silos. For example, one skin doctor asked me to tell my Specialist treating high blood sugar levels to, *"Find out why the immune system was attacking my body?"* When I told the Specialist, the reply was, *"Dermatologists should stick to dermatology."* Not one specialist asked me, what was happening in my family life or was there anything at work that could be impacting on my health.

Even some church groups that I attended told me and other people who are not healed that: *'you're not putting your problems in God's hands, or this sickness is to build character or that it may not be God's will to heal you physically as God is interested in healing the soul.'*

Shocking, I know. These medical and church views imply that the body, emotions, mind and spirit are all operating separately. Yet, we all recognise, and it is pretty common knowledge that the face is instantaneously flushed when embarrassed. When shamed, the eyes and head are lowered. When speaking publicly, the heart rate increases, the palms become sweaty, and the mouth feels dry. This only shows we have instantaneous physical reactions to our emotional states and from our attitudes, beliefs, and feelings. Today, medical doctors, and holistic practitioners acknowledge and recognise that our body, emotions, mind and spirit are integrated and work together in unity.

So how did the separation of body, emotions, mind and spirit come about?

In Eastern Medicine, the body, emotions, mind and spirit are seen and recognised as interconnected and interdependent.

Whereas, in the West, since the 17th Century, Rene Descartes, a French Mathematician and Philosopher, popularised the idea that the body and mind were separate entities accepted in the medical and church world.[13]

Medical science is based on evidence-based science; therefore, health professionals provide treatments based on evidence. This means that thinking, emotions and spirituality, spontaneous healing and placebos or relationship issues are not considered in preventative health measures.

Doctors do not always ask their patients if they have work or relationship issues at home when they have medical conditions such as migraine headaches, skin disorders or chronic, painful and ongoing medical ailments.

Often, patients don't think to ask their doctor if other areas of the body are affected when they get treatment for their symptoms. For example, a man has been taking mood stabilising medications for more than ten years.

He had not been informed that there are links between mood disorders and the digestive system. The microorganisms in the gut can cause changes in how our brains react.[14]

His mood significantly improved after making these few lifestyle changes: removing toxins that caused inflammation from his environment, restoring good bacteria with probiotics, diet change and supplements.[15]

Why does it matter to see the body, emotions, mind and spirit working in union?

Our organs work in unison, constantly giving us messages about how the body functions and what we need to do.
Mental health conditions such as anxiety and depression are often connected to dysfunction in the digestive system. Aggression, disruptive behaviours and learning are also aligned or interconnected to gut bacteria and deficiency in Vitamins B, D, Iron, Omega 3, Magnesium and Zinc. Skin disorders, constipation, and many other chronic conditions are also often associated with a disrupted digestive system and gut bacteria.

When we perceive a threat, the **Sympathetic Nervous System** is automatically activated. Adrenaline and numerous other chemicals are released to alert us and help us handle the threat by fight, flight or freeze.

When the **Sympathetic Nervous System** is activated then the whole body is affected. The heart rate, breathing, blood pressure and glucose levels increase, pupils dilate, and more blood is sent to the brain and muscles preparing the body for action.

The stress response is activated whenever you are: distressed, scared, frightened, stressed-out over an emotional problem or even family events. It is also important to know that there is such a thing as good stress: such as preparing for a wedding, the birth of a child, purchasing a new house or car or even falling in love. Your body still reacts the same way, the Sympathetic Nervous System is activated. The good stress is known as *eustress and still gets your heart rate raised and can raise blood pressure*. When there are high demands physically, mentally and emotionally, both good and bad, the Sympathetic Nervous System kicks in.

However, when the threat is perceived to be over then the **Parasympathetic Nervous System** unconsciously kicks in and puts the brakes on the stress response. Again, all areas of the body are affected when the Parasympathetic Nervous System is activated.

The heart and breathing slow down, pupils constrict, blood flow slows down and glucose levels decrease and numerous chemical changes as the body starts to relax and leave that high state of alert.[16]

Knowing that we are integrated beings means that when we have symptoms, we can relieve the discomfort and find out how the symptoms are connected to the rest of the body. We can find the root cause; for example, headaches, upset stomach or irritable bowel symptoms may be related to relationship conflicts. Feeling dissatisfied or perceiving that life is boring or unfulfilled is a perfect time to look at which area needs nurturing to keep our genes expressed or lit up.

External and environmental factors can influence the way our genes are regulated.

This speaks to the age-old question:

"Is it Nature or Nurture?"

This is part of the exciting and evolving field of genetics known as **Epigenetics**. This is an additional layer of instructions that lies *'on top of"* DNA, controlling how the genes are read and expressed or whether genes are lit up (expressed) or switched off (suppressed).[17]

Wellness is about connecting to all areas of life and to feeling healthy, vibrant and enjoying a fulfilling life.

How the body is integrated is documented in Biblical scriptures.

"A heart at peace gives life to the body, but envy rots the bones."

Proverbs 14:30

"Fear and trembling came upon me, and trembling made all my bones shake."

Job 4.14

"My life is consumed by anguish and my years by groaning, and my strength fails because of my affliction and my bones grow weak."

Psalm 31.10

I would like to invite you to:

Ask questions. For example, where else does this health condition impact?

Ask yourself or a health practitioner:

- "What else can I do while taking medications?
- What effect will this medication have on me?

- What are the side effects?"
- How long will I be on this for?
- Are there any foods that I should avoid that may interact with this medication?

Don't be afraid to ask your doctor, health practitioner or even your pharmacist any questions you may have. This is about YOU!!!

Remember to ask if there is anything you can do regarding lifestyle choices which are outlined in Chapter 9 Nurture Your Inside?

Would they recommend counselling or health coaching, meditation or even social activities with friends?

When it comes to your overall health, there are no bad questions.

When you often feel stressed or overwhelmed: rate or assess all the different areas of your life: relationships, work, finances, environment, physical, emotional, mental and spiritual life.

I like to use the 1 to 10 Rating Method

If you are feeling between 1- 4 then it is considered very little joy or maybe even stressful. Between 4-6 is considerable stress levels and between 7-9 is usually a healthy amount of stress in your day or life.

If you are rating a 10 then this is bliss, happiness and contentment.

Once you evaluate where you are feeling, you can consciously reflect on what you want to change.

The following chapters will give you many examples of actions that you can take to advocate for your own health. I hope to show you how to manifest and create health and vitality in your life moving forward from the inside out.

Chapter 3

The Outside World Follows the Inside World

Rumi, a 13th Century Poet wrote, *"What you seek is seeking you."*[18] Modern interpreters see it as 'you attract what you think.' This has been one of the principles of the *Law of Attraction*.

This quote is interpreted in Farsi and English as "What you seek is within you." This is interpreted as Know Yourself: purpose, your potential and connection to yourself, others and God who is inside. Looking inside and finding out who you are will reveal your authentic essence.

How does the Outer World follow the Inner World?

You may have heard this many times, the *'Outer world follows the Inner world.'* When our outer world is chaotic and life is not going the way you want, and if you feel stuck, go to the mirror.

The outer world is a reflection of our inner world. How we think and feel about ourselves comes from our sense of self-worth.

Our inner world is everything going on inside us: thoughts, feelings, beliefs, memories, values and desires that are hidden from others. Our outer world comprises the things we can see, other people, personal experiences and social interactions, culture, media and economy.

"It is easier to ascribe your feelings to events in the world than to admit that the conditions of the world reflect your feelings. However, it is eternally true that the outside mirrors the inside."[19]

Neville Goddard, Spiritual Teacher on Manifestation

If our inner world is chaotic, this effect spills into all areas of life. Our houses, work desks, filing cabinets, and even the handbag can be cluttered.

It is hard to focus and finish tasks as we are often busy being always busy. We can get tangled in dramas, distractions and do things that take us away from what is most important and procrastinate; never completing or finishing our tasks or finalising what we want to do.

We could be easily irritated, angry or resentful, depleting us of energy and creating disease and biochemical changes.

For example, I worked with high achievers. They work hard and fast, delivering their work on time to the outside world; however, on the inside, many of these high achievers do not feel calm inside.

Often, they feel exhausted, cynical of the system, unhappy with their work and feel overwhelmed much of the time.

Many of them say, *"I can't get on top of things, and I have so much work to do."* In addition, some of them are being treated for eczema, psoriasis, headaches, high blood pressure and many other symptoms, but not looking for the causes. They are unaware of what happens in their body when stressed and do not know how to get their body to restore. Their bodies give them messages such as being on top of the world or burdened, demoralised or

disheartened, however they haven't learned to listen to the messages from their bodies.

I noticed that some of them look outside for solutions and answers. They change diets, fitness routines, jobs, take holidays, self-improvement and fitness programs. Their outside world is relentlessly changing. They get anxious when they hear the news about the economy and world events.

Instead of looking inside for what needs to change, they juggle everything in the outside world, feeling unfulfilled, powerless and stressed out but they end up getting accustomed to the feelings of stress, feeling unwell and think it is normal.

They also think they do not have time to deal with stress. They are not aware or ignore that the body is signalling that something is out of alignment. It's like the red light is flashing but no one is listening!

However, when we become aware of that:

'Twisting in the gut, jittery feeling, being on edge, heavy aches in the chest, constipation, headaches' and start to realise, things are not okay on the inside. We begin to experience a shift in energy.'

When you read Chapters 5 & 6, you will see how our thoughts and emotions express (turn on) or suppress (turn off) genes.

Knowing whether we are anxious, calm, composed or chaotic on the inside allows us to become aware of our thoughts and feelings. It then will allow us to choose and maintain more life-generating and replenishing emotions, increasing calmness, energy, focus, fulfilment, joy, and peace of mind.

The Outside World won't bother or irritate or frighten you so much.

Creating the Future in the Inside World

Gregg Braden, Neuroscience educator and author of Human By Design: *From Evolution By Chance To Transformation by Choice* describes on a You Tube video, how a woman with bladder cancer where medical doctors said they couldn't do anything went to a non-medical hospital in Beijing, China.

Three practitioners started chanting one word and experienced the feeling as if the cancer had gone as the woman had an ultrasound. In less than three minutes, the cancer disappeared. The word that they chanted is translated to *"Already happened or done." The language that the three practitioners used had to match the feeling in their heart as if the healing had already happened. From the inside world, we can create change on the outside.*[20]

This video can be viewed on YouTube, *"Bladder cancer dissolved in three minutes."*

In Dr. Joe Dispenza's book, "**Breaking the Habit of Being Yourself,** *How to lose your mind and create a new one,*" Dr. Dispenza says that 'when he broke his back in six places, he was given a poor prognosis. He decided not to have the surgery. He thought that *'the power who made the body would heal his body.'*

He constructed every vertebra in his mind for at least three hours daily, and his motor function returned and back on his feet in ten weeks.

'When we change our thoughts and feelings, wellbeing increases, epigenetic change occurs on the inside, and it begins to alter your outer presentation.'[21]

I would like to invite you to:

Tune in to your inner world. Self-awareness is the key to transforming stress and creating the future you want.

Reflect on how much time you spend thinking or doing things you do not want instead of what you want.

What emotions do you feel when you are engaged with your peer group, social media and news? Is it beneficial to your good health and welfare? Are they adding to your anxiety or lifting you up?

Take time to reflect on, "What is my body trying to tell me? What is this health issue teaching me?"

"If any of you lacks wisdom, you should ask God, who gives generously to all without finding fault, and it will be given to you."

James 1.5

Chapter 4

Imagination and Feelings are the Secret to Perfect Health

"*Your imagination is the preview of your life.*"

Albert Einstein, Physicist

Often, when people are asked what wellness or being healed looks like, they say, *"I don't want to have the disease."* However, there is little thought about what not having the disease would look like.

The focus is on what we don't want, not what we do want. Imagine what it would feel like when you can walk and not feel breathless, or you can walk and not use a wheelchair? What would it feel like where you are free to check your blood sugars less often because your sugar levels are stable?

Many people cannot visualise being really well. When asked why it is difficult to visualise being really well, some people say, *"Imagining is airy-fairy, only children imagine, it's not concrete or practical because some diseases cannot be changed."*

Yet imagination and feeling *as if you already have the outcome are powerful.*

"The person with dreams is more powerful than the one with all the facts."[22]

Albert Einstein, Physicist

Stephen Covey, author of, **The Seven Habits of Highly Effective People**, says *"Success starts with the end in mind. Things are created first in the mind and then in the physical."*[23] Business Leaders are encouraged to follow this visualising habit and imagine the outcome creating huge success. Does this work outside the corporate business?

Yes! Professional athletes imagine themselves winning the gold medal or arriving first at the finish line. Many Olympic Athletes work with sports Psychologists to practice imagining their bodies doing different actions, for example, jumping in the air on skis in the snow. They even imagine their body moving in different weather conditions and they imagine hearing the roar of the spectators cheering and seeing themselves on the podium accepting and receiving their gold medal for months and sometimes years before the actual event or competition.

The unconscious mind works toward the images they have created.[24]

"Your mind says, your brain loves to imagine to: visualise ideas, find solutions, imaginative responses to a number of fascinating neural mechanisms. The neuroscience of imagination tells us that there is a creative genius inside us. Allow the brain to daydream, create new worlds and relieve the tensions and problems in your life, solve problems and clarify your dreams."[25]

Valerie Sabater, Psychologist

Are you still not sure about imagination? Look up when you see a plane; Orville and Wilbur Wright imagined they could fly. They flew for 12 seconds for 37 meters in 1903, because of them, we can travel from continent to continent in hours.

"When imagination and excitement are mixed together, you will either not notice obstacles, or they will be largely diminished and, therefore, your courage will increase!" [26]

Shana Schutte, Focus on the Family

We can create a new state of health by thinking, believing and feeling like we already have it. It's going into the future, coming back to the present with memories of the future, and living as if we are already healed.

"God gives life to the dead and calls into being things that were not."

Romans 4.17

Dayna Belcher, **Kingdom Builders Academy Success Coach**, says, "*Visualising the future and calling it into existence is prophetic living.*" Dayna gave me the following steps to follow. They are one of the most valuable keys to manifesting that I can share with you."

Step 1: Visualise the future

Step 2: Believe

Step 3: Act

Step 4: It comes forth

How does it work?

Dr. Joe Dispenza, author of **Breaking the Habit of Being Yourself** says, *'To set a clear intention of the outcome we want with a feeling as if it has already happened and repeat it often. Our inner world will repeatedly experience healing through our thoughts and feelings. This will then manifest in the outer world.'*

Dr. Dispenza gives an example where a group in their 80's in a research study started living as if they were young, listening to music and reading from their younger years. In documented cases, within four days, they started signalling the exact genetic change to reflect who they were becoming. This resulted in epigenetic changes. Their bodies showed biologically they were 22 years younger.[27]

Neuroscientist Dr. Donald Hebb explains what happens with neurons telling a new story opens our minds to other perspectives, *"As the neurons fire, neurotransmitters with this new information will be absorbed by the cells next to them. Over time these synaptic transmissions will become automatic and stronger, resulting in biological changes."*[28]

"Very often, the only way to get a quality reality is to start behaving as if you already had it." [29]

C.S Lewis, Author of Classics, Lay Theologian

For about six months, I meditated, believing *'I was already at one with God and that the power of God was within.'*

I imagined that my skin, which had Vitiligo all over my body for more than two years, had healed.

I imagined my skin was radiant with my original colour, with no depigmentation.

I imagined myself with bare arms, smiling, laughing, and feeling the joy of being myself (no concealing creams or long sleeves). In the beginning and when I started my journey of healing, I used to doubt a lot, especially when I couldn't see any improvements right away. I also got put off by comments like *"it's all psycho mumbo jumbo,"* a young pharmacist told me very clearly that Type 2 Diabetes was a forever condition and that I would be on insulin for the rest of my life. Although this comment took my joy away, my spirit leapt in me and I asked her, *"why would you take hope away from your customers?"*

I saw how shocked she was at my comment. I knew she had never considered that her words could bring or take away hope. This only reinforced my determination to keep hope alive and not let anyone take it away. I persisted, thanking God every day for the outcome I imagined.

Whenever I doubted or felt discouraged, I remembered the farmer who sowed seeds after the rains. Farmers don't look every day to see if the crop is growing. They planted the seeds, cultivated the soil and environment, did the work, watered and fed nutrients to the land and believe they know that there will be a harvest.

I also imagined my hair had grown back, my blood sugar levels, and biochemistry were in a healthy range, I saw myself being happy, smiling, full of vitality and skipping, living a healthy life living as if I was already healed.

My hair grew back, and I had more control over my biochemistry. There was no more need for me to have medication for blood pressure and or Type 2 diabetes. That is correct, no insulin. And yay-the Vitiligo has gone, my skin is healed!!!

This is Biohacking or Cell Mastery

Biohacking means making changes in your body with diet, exercise, positive thinking and shifting negative emotions. Technology, like monitoring heart rate, blood pressure, reminders to walk, or hydrate are lifestyle changes that bring changes in your body.

I would like to invite you to:

Imagine you have changed your life and your health has improved. See yourself as healthy, vibrant and whole in the inside and the outside.

Pray, say an affirmation or declaration or meditate, if you feel that you doubt that you are not healed. Any action you take will lift your spirits and raise your energy levels.

Imagine, believe, and feel as if healing has already happened from the inside out.

Part 2

How Our Genes Turn On and Off

Chapter 5

How Beliefs Control Our Lives

"The secret of life is not a secret at all. It is not our genes but our beliefs that control our lives." [30]

Dr. Bruce Lipton, Cellular Biologist

My mother, who was 93 years old, often asked me when I would do a PhD like my sister had done. That question always filled me with frustration. I used to feel so frustrated with my mother as I told her I had no desire to do a PhD degree. But she continued to ask me. At first, I thought she did not approve of me or that she did not think I amounted to much. I also thought she had no clue about the time and expense involved, so I always steered the conversation away from the topic.

Then one day she asked me again. I noted her tone; she was insistent. When I looked at her, I was just about to say, please don't ask me this again. Her face was soft and kind. So, I said, *"Would you have done this study, mum?"* She immediately said, *"No! I am too stupid!"* What!

My mother was a school teacher. She said:

"I was asked by my manager, when I first came to Australia to get a further qualification to go into management, but I didn't. I thought I was too stupid, but I should have done it. I pushed you to study and achieve because I didn't do it myself."

We then discussed all the missed opportunities because of our low opinion of ourselves. The belief that, "*I am not good enough*" has been embedded in me since childhood. I remember how anxious I would be to show my school report to my father. The school report was graded on how I achieved and ranked against others in the class. When I came second or third in the class, my dad would say, "*I expect you to come first.*" I tried and tried. A few times, I came; first, my dad would say, "*Keep it up.*" That's what I did, striving until I burnt out in midlife.

As a primary school student, the class captains would pick their teams for different sports. Always last, I was only picked when no one else was left. This happened every week in school from the age of eight for more than five years. I felt so deficient, not good enough, rejected and humiliated. *Do you know what I mean* and how I felt about myself?

This is only one example of the shame and not feeling worthy from a very early age. There were so many more experiences from my childhood that reinforced feelings of powerlessness, shame especially at school and not knowing how to change problematic situations.

By the time I had turned around the age of seven, I would sit with my parents at the dining room table as they allocated the budget for all the bills they had to pay from their monthly salary.

My job was to tie a rubber band around the allocated cash after my mother wrote on a note what the money was for. However, the money would run out before the end of the month, resulting in arguments, always about money.

As a young child, I would feel so worried and powerless because I did not know how to fix the problem or help make it better. I disliked arguments as I felt anxious as I wanted everyone around me to be happy and to get along.

Often, I would accompany my mother to the pawn shop where mum would borrow money to pay for private school and college fees, leaving her gold ring and chain. Then after payday, my mum returned to collect her jewellery and paid more because the interest of the loan was very high. I can remember this happening many times over a few years when we were still in India, and I was only a young child.

My dad also felt that he was not good enough when he migrated to Australia at the age of 53 years. He was unemployed for a long period of time, taking hard physical work much below his skillset to care for and support his family.

Three years later, he had a stroke and was no longer able to work and support his family. He felt depressed and discouraged because life as he had planned and dreamed about would not be what he thought it to be.

After a few years, dad started driving again and returned to an almost normal everyday life, although he was not able to return to work. Dad believed that he had to be the provider for his family. Due to this belief of having to be the bread- winner in the home, it took the spark out of him, and he died at 59.

From early childhood, I picked up beliefs that ran silently in my subconscious. "*There was no one to provide for me. I did not know how to make money except to earn it in a job. I don't have enough.*"

I avoided situations and opportunities with the risk of feeling rejected or humiliated. I strived to excel and criticised myself harshly when I did not meet my expectations. I kept silent and didn't stand up for myself as I detested conflict and avoided it at all costs. In retrospect, I was so compliant that I stayed sitting in boring, long lectures and church sermons when all I wanted to do was get away.

Why do our beliefs matter?

When the perceptions of parents, teachers and spiritual leaders are accepted, they are programmed into the subconscious mind and hardwired in the brain.

We accept these perceptions as accurate, influencing our attitudes, behaviours, biology, choices, decision-making, and emotions. These programmed perceptions create our reality for the rest of our lives unless we become aware of them and reprogram them.

However, not all perceptions are accurate, especially when teachers tell young students they won't amount to anything or are stupid. Imagine this misperception is programmed in the subconscious mind. Is there any wonder that this belief influences limiting behaviour?

Spiritual beliefs give us hope and guidance, and peace of mind. However, suppose Church leaders teach personal preferences or convictions as Biblical facts or truth. In that case, our thinking becomes distorted about God and what we think of ourselves and other people.

The Medical Journal of Australia, reported in 2021 that Placebos (which is positive thinking and beliefs) that the treatment will heal should be part of medical care.[31]

However, did you know that negative thinking can be destructive?

A case study by Dr. Clifton Meador had a patient diagnosed with oesophageal cancer who died a few weeks later. On autopsy, there was no trace of oesophageal cancer, although he had a few spots in his liver and one spot in his lung. Everyone thought cancer killed him. However, Dr. Meador said, *"His patient died with cancer but not from cancer."*

He died because he believed he was going to die.[32]

"If you believe you can, or if you believe you can't, you're right."[33]

Henry Ford

When we constantly hear how dangerous our world is, we scare ourselves with the worst case scenario, fear-based thinking: "*What if something awful happens? What will people think? We run from opportunities that have a possibility of rejection, humiliation or pain we've been carrying because of our beliefs. We then hide, keep silent, and do not take the opportunities to become all we can be or rise to our calling and use the gifts we've been given to share with others."*

Negative thoughts deplete energy. Subconscious programs run in the background. Neuroscience research confirms that these programs keep us from reaching our goals. Have you wondered why people with a considerable body shape and weight transformation end up putting on all the body weight lost? That's why weight loss programs now include changing subconscious beliefs around food, eating, and self-worth.

Illness can have benefits for a person who is chronically ill. For example, Mary felt unwell on the weekends.

She had many investigations but could not find an answer. Eventually, she saw a Psychologist who found out that her husband wanted to go to social events on the weekends. It was on the weekends that Mary was unwell.

Mary said to the Psychologist: *"I don't want to go out because I am not a good communicator."*

The Psychologist delved a little bit more. Mary then said, *"I hate going to social events, I hate how I look."* She felt sad and embarrassed and thought she was not good enough compared to the other friends. When her belief about herself was addressed, her confidence increased, and she started going out to social events with her husband.

Secondary benefits for illness are documented in medical and psychology journals. For example, sexual avoidance has been recorded as a benefit of chronic illness across all genders.

Mental Health Professionals talk about the *sick role that many people take on.* A person can take on a sick role to cope with whatever situation they perceive that they are dealing with. However, it may not continue to serve them now as the conditions may have changed. They may have learned this behaviour early in life or taking on the sick role may have come down the family line.[34]

Family therapists report that a sick role is taken on, so that the focus is on the sick person rather than dealing with the real causes, stresses or dysfunction in the family dynamics.[35]

Truly, I was unaware that I had adopted a *sick role* in my family. It wasn't until investigations were made by a medical team that included an invasive examination under anesthetic were performed. I was actually surprised that I had learned this behaviour years ago in order to cope with my family relationships and dynamics.

My husband experienced depression when my children were under the age of five. This lasted for many years. I remember experiencing severe abdominal pain and vomiting and my husband stepped up and functioned very well whenever I was ill.

Abdominal pain became a regular pattern for me. I was later diagnosed with Irritable Bowel Syndrome and soon became aware of why I was displaying these symptoms.

I learned that the symptoms I was experiencing resulted from a subconscious program that appeared to benefit me as my body was able to rest from the high stress I was experiencing. The result was that I felt cared for when I was ill. Once I became aware of the sick role I was experiencing, I learned to choose more helpful self-care strategies.

My husband received care and recovered. Amazingly, that's when my abdominal pain stopped. In retrospect, I can actually understand and see the benefit the illness brought me. Yet, I do not condemn myself for taking a sick role, this was a lesson and a learning journey that I was on with my family.

Please do not judge yourself or others harshly for *these **sick role** beliefs. Instead, see yourself or someone you think may have this issue with compassion and understanding.*

Often, this is a way of coping with a highly distressing situation or difficult family dynamics. Adapting a sick role may have been the way to survive and is an unconscious belief.

When assessing your own health and situation, give yourself grace. There are many reasons why you could have illnesses that have resulted from toxins in the environment, infections or associated with a disability from birth or an injury. Not everyone has a secondary benefit. However, changing our thinking is essential if we want to reclaim our health.

According to Dr. Ken Blue's book, **Authority to Heal,** *he discusses, 'A mind-body connection causes sickness.'* Dr. Blue also works with people who have been involved in the occult.

He emphasises the importance *"to get rid of the roots and clean up the beliefs that keep us in emotional pain".*[36]

It is also possible to change the health conditions of others through our beliefs. Dr. Blue also says, *'That people who pray for other people believe God is willing to heal, and they operate from compassion. They allow themselves to be conduits or intercessors.'*

Recall the story in Chapter three; the practitioners who worked with the woman with bladder cancer in Beijing, permitted themselves to be conduits as they chanted from their hearts, believing the healing had already happened.

HeartMath research confirms that compassion and unconditional love is carried through the heart's electromagnetic field to other people and that will lift their vibration.[37]

How to change your DNA

Dr. Bruce Lipton in his book, **The Biology of Beliefs**: *Unleashing the Power of Consciousness, Matter & Miracles* states, *"Our beliefs act as a filter between the natural environment and our biology. If we use dark filters, it turns everything black and makes our bodies susceptible to disease. This causes our bodies to shut down as we go into a protective mode. When we see everything black, our bodies become susceptible to disease. Genes that express themselves to keep the body functioning will go out."*

Dr. Bruce Lipton, a Cellular Biologist and author says, *"If we see the world with rose-coloured glasses, our cells flourish."*[38]

In the **HeartMath** article, **You can change your DNA**, the researchers determined that intentional *positive thought can influence physical aspects of DNA strands.*[39]

How Do We Think Of Ourselves?

"What sort of relationship are you having with your body when you hate yourself, think poorly about yourself? What messages are you giving to your cells? If you believe you are sick, your cells are listening." [40]

Louise Hay, Love Your Body

Research from Japan by Dr. Masaru Emoto, demonstrates, '*negative thoughts and words over water crystals resulted in them being disoriented and chaotic.*' However, '*when positive comments and words of love and gratitude were poured over it, the water crystals became orderly, geometric, and intricate.*'[41]

Your beliefs become your thoughts. Your thoughts become your words. Your words become your actions. Your actions become your habits. Your habits become your values. Your values become your destiny. [42]

Mahatma Gandhi

Yes, our Conscious and Unconscious beliefs control our lives.

Numerous **Biblical Scriptures** give us directions to change our thinking.

Some examples from the Bible:

"Be transformed by the renewing of your mind."

Romans 12.2

"We have the mind of Christ."

1 Corinthians 2.16

Capture your thinking."

2 Corinthians 10.5

"Be careful how you think; your life is shaped by your thoughts."

Proverbs 4. 23

I would like to invite you to:

Become aware and notice the words that you say and use both out loud and silently to yourself. WORDS HAVE POWER. THOUGHTS HAVE POWER.

For example, if you worry about worst-case scenarios, instead of saying "*What if it happens", one way to change this is to say, what if something wonderful happens?*"

Consider the kind of relationship you have with yourself, your body and others?

Chapter 6

Emotions Build or Destroy Health

Emotions can be intense and can feel pleasant or unpleasant. Emotions give us messages about how we feel *or if something **is** wrong in the body.*

Emotions are associated with thoughts, sensations and biochemical reactions.

Over 1400 biochemical changes are set in motion by our changing emotions. Among these biochemical changes is the release of hormones. Two of the hormones produced are Cortisol, the "stress hormone", and DHEA," the vitality hormone" once produced in the body have a long-lasting effect. Depleting emotions increases cortisol production and renewing emotions increases DHEA. [43]

Dr. Rollin McCraty PhD HeartMath Resilience Program

Emotions such as frustration, anxiety, anger, and fear are depleting, negative or survival emotions. They drain energy and, if long-lasting, reduce our quality of life. Heart rhythms are affected and are incoherent. Replenishing emotions such as love, compassion, appreciation, and joy increase energy and vitality, and the heart rhythms are coherent.

Unexpressed or repressed emotions get lodged in the body, resulting in organs not working at their best. Even if we don't express our emotions, it doesn't mean our bodies are not reacting to the feelings we are having.

Think about the tension in your shoulders and neck aches and migraine pain. If these emotions accumulate, they impact the function of the organs making us ill and can often keep us sick.

Emotions affect our behaviour and judgement. People buy products based on their feelings. Advertisers know this well. However, we are not always aware of what we are feeling. It is hard to identify when there is a mix of feelings. We may have learned to suppress our emotions, especially if we were criticised or hurt physically, for showing our feelings.

If we stay in an emotion too long, it becomes part of our personality. Sunshine personalities are described as a breath of fresh air, having high energy and joy. Compare that to the person who is a complainer, criticiser or provoker. How do they get described?

How do Emotions make or keep us sick?

Emotions can build or destroy your health. The following information on emotions shows how they can destroy health.

The longer we stay in these emotions, the more energy is depleted, and we are in a survival state.

These emotions generate more negative thoughts, and it keeps us stuck in a low vibration attracting more experiences in life like the thoughts that match the emotion increasing the feeling of stress. Elevated and sustained stress can reduce immunity and increase the risk of heart disease, chronic pain and depression and other diseases.

Anger

When we are angry, **Adrenaline** and **Cortisol** are released into the body. Circulating adrenaline increases blood pressure and circulating stress hormones raise blood sugar levels, muscle weakness and impact on mood swings.

Have you ever felt churned up after an argument or some event that you have experienced?

Did you know that it takes approximately twelve hours for Cortisol to leave the body. Cortisol is often released early in the morning and when feeling stressed due to high emotional demands.

The increase of hormones being released is known to accelerate ageing, increases heart disease, reduces mental functioning and overall weakens immunity.

Anger is not wrong. When we are angry it tells us when our boundaries have been violated, compromised or and if someone is controlling, abusing or not valuing us.

Many have learned to channel the energy constructively and mobilise to fight against injustice. Remember, it is the accumulation of anger, constant stress, and the feeling of being condemned, picked on and criticised that destroys health or ultimately leads to outward rage.

We know what anger looks like; clenched fists, intimidating posture, and tensed body language or even raised voice, yelling and screaming. However, when someone constantly focuses on negative experiences, criticises, blames, shames, is impatient, irritable, resentful, bitter or hostile, these are all signs of internal anger being displayed outwardly.

Unexpressed anger accumulates and, if not expressed, impacts health too. Symptoms can include chronic pain, stomach, joint pain, rapid heart rate, high blood pressure, reduced immunity, migraines, low vision and even some cancers.

The longer we stay angry, the longer the Cortisol keeps circulating in the body.

No wonder. Recall the biblical scriptures Ephesians 4: 31, written around 60 AD, so profoundly states:

"Let all bitterness, wrath, anger, clamour (outrage) and slander be removed, along with all malice."

Bitterness and / or Resentment

Bitterness and Resentment are linked to anger and outrage. It is about feeling powerless, let down by someone or something and not being able to change things. It can be taken into every relationship. It can lead to constantly thinking of the wrong and that there is no joy in living now. Bitterness affects the body functions including metabolism, breathing, heart rate and even the overall immune system.

Anxiety and Fear

A perceived threat will activate the **Sympathetic Nervous System** for fight, flight or freeze. Stress hormones are immediately released into the body. This response is an unconscious survival reaction that happens for our survival. If the perceived threat continues or becomes frequent, the body we will be in and possibly stay in survival mode for extended lengths of time. That is when something has to give and often stomach, and bowel upsets flare up and continue to worsen.

The stress hormones circulate throughout the body organs: and the adrenaline, cortisol and many other stress hormones are released into the bloodstream and remember, it takes more than twelve hours for these hormones to leave the body.

This can lead to a higher incidence of heart rate rhythm disturbances, stomach or irritable bowel symptoms, mood swings; emotional outbursts often result in Post-Traumatic Stress.

Guilt

Intense guilt can cause emotional and physical pain, headaches, and aches in almost any area of the body. Sometimes, people feel guilty whether they did something wrong or not. Guilt can eat people up from the inside out as they judge themselves. This can lead to self-rejection and self-hatred and always self-judgement.

Sometimes we make decisions or assumptions and don't live the lives we want because we want to avoid hurting someone else or ourselves. Often people react out of guilt by assuming terrible consequences to their actions. It's important to recognise that Guilt and Fear are the two main reasons that people suffer silently inside; not wanting to hurt others or cause them pain, grief, illness or even life- threatening conditions.

That is a lot of stress to put on a person's body for extended lengths of time. Many people suffer in silence because they fear hurting others by their decisions or actions. What if that other person becomes ill or worse yet, could possibly die?

That is a lot of stress to carry around on the inside of your body, mind and spirit.

Shame

According to **The National Foundation for Cancer Research**, shame is a big trigger of the central stress response system. The feeling of shame results in biochemical changes that increase inflammation and decrease immunity.

Research clearly states that there is a direct correlation between shame to cancer progression, diabetes, heart disease and numerous other chronic illnesses.[44]

Dr. Joe Dispenza in his book **Becoming Supernatural**, *How Uncommon People are Doing the Uncommon* says, *"Everything in our material universe gives off light and information. When we are just in survival mode, we are burdened by the effects of stress and hormones. The field around us shrinks, and the light goes dim."*

The genes do not express themselves in their best way in survival mode. Joe Dispenza says, *"When more light is emitted, there's more energy and hence more life. When people have less light and information surrounding their body, they are more matter, emitting less vital energy."*[45]

Different cells within our bodies vibrate at different frequencies. However, they change with illness, how we think or feel, or what we eat or when we experience sustained stress.

When there is a lower frequency, the energy becomes dense and dark and it becomes harder to solve problems, and often confusion and pain is experienced. Emotions are stored in organs and muscles resulting in reducing our wellbeing.

The higher the vibrations, the healthier and lighter a person feels. There is more light in the energy. Everything seems to flow, and this is the state where manifestation occurs.

How emotions repair DNA

Emotions produce a vibration that affects our health and the people around us. The vibrations attract *like* vibrations; if we are angry, we attract more things to be angry about. Our thoughts create the chemicals that match our thoughts.

Then we think more thoughts that match the feeling. This means we bathe in the emotional chemical that floods the body.

So, if we have positive thoughts and replenishing emotions like; compassion, joy, love, gratitude, and peace, more light is given off, and the organs vibrate more effectively and efficiently.

According to the **HeartMath** article on their website, **Raising Our Vibrations Through Compassion and Unconditional Love**:

"When our vibrations are up, we respond to stressful situations with soundness, resilience and clearer discernment. We are less vulnerable to frustration, impatience, anger, and anxiety. We feel more self-secure and less critical of others and ourselves."

"When we sincerely have feelings such as appreciation, compassion, love and gratitude, we activate the power of the heart. The heart's electrical energy calms us down, bringing focus and peace, and nourishes the body at a cellular level."

"These emotions are known as elevated emotions as they have a higher vibration. When we use techniques to calm ourselves down whilst experiencing these elevated emotions and intentionally thinking positive thoughts, we can influence the body at the cellular level by unwinding and influencing DNA repair."[46]

Love/Compassion/Gratitude

According to **HeartMath** research and thousands of case studies:

The higher the vibrations, the healthier and lighter a person feels. There is more light in the energy. Everything seems to flow, and this is the state where manifestation occurs.

"Unconditional love and compassion are among the highest vibrations of love. Many people realise that unconditional love and compassion are from our higher consciousness potentials required for healing. However, it's a way of being that transforms everything."

In his book **Letting Go**, *The Pathway to Surrender,* Dr. David Hawkins says, *"Lovingness is a way of life that transforms everything around us because of the radiation of that energy."*[47]

Forgiveness

Forgiveness is also an aspect of love. It is better for us if we forgive from our hearts, not out of duty. The **Mayo Clinic** writes about forgiveness's benefits: healthier relationships and less anxiety, lower blood pressure, fewer symptoms of depression, a stronger immune system, improved health and better self-esteem.[48]

Self-Compassion

Self-compassion is directing compassion to yourself. This soothes the body and mind.

Self-compassion helps to overturn that inner voice within us all. That voice that criticises, condemns our thoughts and actions in us all, which often fuels self-hatred. Remember what survival emotions do to the body. Self-compassion soothes the body and mind and puts the brakes on the stress response, overturning the inner criticising voice within you that may be fuelling self-hatred.

When you feel calmer, there is clarity and that provides the ability to make better, clear thinking and compassionate, empowering decisions.

Sometimes it's hard to be self-compassionate because of the stress we feel, or we think we are being selfish.

Gratitude

Gratitude rewires the neuronal pathway and lights up neurons, so we start to feel pleasure. As soon as we are grateful, there is an increase in the levels of activity in the hypothalamus (within the brain), which influences appetite, sleep, metabolism and stress levels.[49]

Gratitude is a powerful expression of the heart. When we are grateful, the heart initiates the neuronal activity, not the other way around. To have a feeling of gratitude puts the brakes on the stress response and creates a state of coherence.

This is when thoughts and emotions are in balance, inner calmness, clearer thinking under pressure and increased ability to handle everyday stress.

It is easy to feel gratitude when everything is going well in life. However, when stressed, we tend to focus on negative thoughts and end up triggering and sustaining the stress response that causes wear and tear on the body.

When we say we are grateful without feeling, we still end up frustrated, anxious, judgmental and stuck. *If you express or feel heartfelt gratitude, you create a reservoir of deep peace, creative solutions and energy.*

Laughter

Dr. Norman Cousins, in his book, **Anatomy of an Illness,** healed himself from a severe and life-threatening disease. He was hospitalised with near severe paralysis of his legs. He states, "*Deep down, I knew I had a good chance and relished the idea of bucking the odds.*"

He said, *"The key to his recovery was 10 minutes of genuine belly laughter which gave him at least two hours of pain-free sleep."* He requested the nurses read to him excerpts from humour columns and show him old Marx Brothers movies. Cousins described this as the *Placebo Effect*.

He says that *"This is not a substitute for medical care, but that laughter is the best medicine."*[50]

"A merry heart does good like a medicine, but a broken spirit dries the bones."

Proverbs 17:22

Regenerating Emotions (elevated emotions) activate the **Parasympathetic Nervous System** and put the brakes on the stress response, decreasing the stress hormones and increasing the release of oxytocin, DHEA (vitality hormone) and an overall feeling of ease. This process allows DNA to continuously heal from the inside out and helps us to live longer, happier and healthier lives.

It gives us a space to pause before reacting, which helps us maintain better relationships.

I invite you to consider:

What are the things you do in your day to increase your replenishing (happy, elevated) emotions and your vibration?

Take time to reflect on the lessons you have learned from this health challenge that you are grateful for and from the place of now.

What do you need to let go?

How much laughter or play is in your day?

Do a quick evaluation of your day ahead so you can plan to increase your laughter, vitality, joy of life and release more youthful hormones. (DHEA)

Chapter 7
Leave the Past Back

"The past is a place of reference, not a place of residence. The past is a place of learning, not a place of living."

Roy T Bennett, ***The Light in the heart***[51]

My 93 year old mother and I went out for a meal every Sunday. We loved chatting together and really enjoyed each other's company. One Sunday, my mother quietly said, "*when I was little, I sat still in my church clothes; if I moved from my chair, I would be hit.*" I was gobsmacked, when I noticed my mother sitting quietly in the chair.

My heart went out to my mother. How sad that this little girl couldn't move out of her chair. She sat in fear. How many Sundays did she dread? How many years did this girl sit terrified? My mother said discipline was harsh in her home, and she said she was fearful at home.

The next day, I had my muscles tested by a health practitioner. When asked about my grandmother, I noticed that I had no strength.

I could not push the Kinesiologist's hands that were pushing down on my forearms.

I was told I was carrying my grandmother's grief. That emotion caught with an unresolved event manifested into physical pain, producing cortisol that can crystalise in organs and create an imbalance in the body.

Not knowing my grandmother, I asked my mother and an older cousin. I found out my grandmother's son died most likely from suicide, and soon after, her husband died. My mother described my grandmother as nervous and said her hands used to shake. My grandmother must have experienced severe grief and anxiety.

My grandmother's husband, the bread-winner of the family, died in 1932. There is no social security in India for widows with children. My grandmother's son died, which would have been unbearable emotional pain. Then, being told it was suicide would have felt devastating. So many survival emotions must have been experienced: fear of the future, guilt, shame, and grief.

How was my mother affected by her mother's suffering and the loss of her brother first and her father when she was only nine years old?

My curiosity increased. I started reading more about how generational trauma like addictions, anxiety, grief, poverty, suicide, violence and even war goes down and is transcended through the generations and turns off genes from expressing themselves for optimum health. How did I carry my grandmother's grief?

How does this happen?

According to Child and Adolescent Health journal, multi-generational trauma is passed down from generation to generation through learned behaviours. Research on the effects of the Holocaust showed that marks on the genes were passed down to their families.[52]

In Jean-Pierre Barral's book, **Understanding the Messages of Your Body**, *How To Interpret Physical and Emotional Signals to Achieve Optimal Health*, says, *"The body retains the memory of trauma. Everything is stored in our unconscious mind."*

Barral says, *'If the emotions are too hot to handle, it gets passed on to the organs. Emotions are lodged in the body especially when they are not expressed or are repressed."*[53]

If an event causes adrenaline and or cortisol to be unconsciously secreted to handle a threat, then the memory is engraved in the mind.

Research shows that pregnant women who are highly stressed increase the risk of disease in the foetus, baby or child. Stress and other extenuating circumstances affect genes being expressed or turned on or even turned off.

Trauma can be a series of small traumas or living in an environment where there is fear, or it can arise from violence or catastrophic events. Our brain records all the emotions and tensions we run into and redistributes them to the body depending on intensity. Knowing when symptoms or a health condition started can help you identify and possibly undo the problem.

However, this is the time for self-compassion. Don't beat yourself up if you are experiencing emotions that are highly distressing, highly aroused and unable to focus or think positively. Most likely the stress response that helps us survive is now still activated, over reactive and not necessary now that the threat is gone.

Martez Schembri in her book, **From Stress to Bliss**, *Journey from Post-Traumatic Stress to Post Traumatic Growth* says, *'if we do not address the painful energy or touch triggers, tissue memory, fearful emotions, thoughts, beliefs and stress, the body can remember and return to those memories again and again.*

She also reassures people experiencing *Post Traumatic Stress that it is a normal reaction to an abnormal event and is a reordering of the neural network and sensory pathways so that one can survive in a really dangerous situation.'*[54]

The priority is to feel safe and do what is needed to feel safe and calm.

Seek support from a professional trained in trauma, a health practitioner, a family member or reach out and utilise the **24 Hour Help Lines** in your local area. See Resources on the page 121.

"For real change to occur, the body needs to learn that the danger has passed and live in the reality of the present." [55]

Bessel Van Der Kolk, Trauma Specialist

Why do we need a new story?

According to Dr. Joe Dispenza in his book, **Breaking the Habit of Being Yourself** says, *'The brain releases chemicals that make your body feel precisely how you think. When we feel exactly like we are thinking, e.g., when we feel sad, we think sad thoughts. We only give rise to more thoughts to make us feel how we think.'*

We then get stuck in a cycle.

Imagine when we wake up, we have no improvement in our health. We could think thoughts like this is not fair, or things are not going to get better. Our thoughts will create the emotions that match the thoughts: anger, bitterness, depression, hopelessness or sadness.

Then more thoughts will occur, matching anger, bitterness or despair. The same thing happens daily, which hardwired the brain in the same pattern over and over again. These depleting negative thoughts do not encourage DNA repair.

Now, imagine if you woke up because you were looking forward to something pleasant. The emotions that match the thoughts would be joyful, happier and replenishing. You would have more energy and lightness.

When we think positive thoughts, elevated emotions match the thoughts. If repeated consistently, there is a new story being hardwired in our brain, DNA and in our inside world that will result in biological changes in our outside world.[56]

We can ask ourselves; How do we want to feel?

How do I want my day to go? Do I want to repair my DNA?

Do I want to have more replenishing emotions to improve my mood, to turn on the lights of my genes so that I restore and function optimally?

Try 60 second solutions to shift emotions.

1. Breathe in the Attitude you want.

   Breathe in the attitude you want, e.g., Calmness and breathe out the feeling you do not wish to have. I breathe in peace and breathe out peace. This technique will put the brakes on the stress response and give enough time to pause before making a decision.

   In 60 seconds, we can interrupt your negative thinking and sad depressive feelings.

2. Peter Sage who developed the **Elite Mentorship Forum** Program teaches, *"Be aware of the feeling, the emotion, and where it is located. It may move. Don't tell yourself you are angry; instead, say I am feeling the emotion of anger.*

   You don't identify with the emotion, Observe and notice when it moves. It will take 60-90 seconds for the emotion to go."[57]

   I do this often as it helps me become aware of what and where the emotion is and how quickly 60 seconds goes by, and that the emotion disappears.

3. Use this **HeartMath** self-regulating technique to reset and bring micro recovery to the body. It stops the stress response. It is called the **Quick Coherence® Technique**

   This technique can help you reset and get micro recovery to your body and halt the stress response and experience inner calmness. Research shows that when a person feels calm on the inside and has positive emotions, the heart's powerful magnetic field transmits peace, caring, kindness and love to others.[58]

Our heart broadcasts how we feel through the electromagnetic field.

"Above all else, guard your heart, for everything you do flows from it."

Proverbs 4. 23

***I would like to invite you to*:**

Use the Quick Coherence® Technique for 60 seconds when your inside feels chaotic and to prepare for any stressful event or high demands.

It can be done with eyes open. Use it anytime, anywhere. Preferably before bed, when you wake up, during lunch and before you enter your house.

Step 1: Heart Focused Breathing

Focus your attention on the area of the heart. Imagine your breath flowing in or out of the heart area. Breathe slower and more deeply than usual.

Step 2: Activate a Positive Feeling

Make a sincere attempt to experience a regenerative feeling, such as appreciation or care for someone or something in your life.

Part 3

Live Freely, Fully and Feel Fantastic

Chapter 8

Nurture The Inside: Fill Your Energy Tanks

Everyone is unique. Some people have allergies, different health conditions that require personalised medical care.

It's important to be aware that one mode of treatment that works for someone else may not suit you. For example, I was given intravenous infusions of NAD+ over a few months for cell recovery. NAD (*Nicotinamide adenine dinucleotide*) which is in every living cell and is essential for enzyme activity and to maintain the health of cells.

However, I had side effects of vomiting and abdominal pain. NAD+ is used widely worldwide; however, I was not able to tolerate it. There is so much information available at the click of a button these days on nutrition, fitness, health symptoms, mental health and pretty much any question you might have. I remember having so much information that overwhelmed me that I ended up not doing anything.

Please reach out and collaborate with your health practitioner. We are all unique individuals and there is not one-fit for all. We all have very different needs and personal treatments that will heal your body from the inside out.

Therefore, this chapter focuses on principles to keep your energy up for vitality and to help your body heal from health conditions from the inside out.

When people say they are feeling exhausted and do not have a physical illness to cause tiredness. It's because they are expending more energy than replacing it.

Relentless emotional and physical demands drain energy and cause dysfunction in the organs when the energy is not renewed.

Some people are not aware of being able to get energy from their emotional, mental, physical and spiritual domains. They are also not aware of energy leaks throughout the day.

When we have our physical and emotional tanks filled, it gives us the courage and the perception that we are in control and can handle the stressful situations and health conditions we face.

This is what **Polar Explorer Richard E Byrd** found when he spent more than five months in the Antarctic dark, and frigidly cold winter. He was studying inland temperatures. In winter, the temperatures were -75 degrees F.

However, Byrd became ill from carbon monoxide poisoning from a malfunctioning stove. He wrote about his experience and his resilience in his book **Alone,** *The Classic Polar Adventure*. Byrd was eventually rescued after five months of suffering from carbon monoxide poisoning. Somehow he found the strength to live and survive horrific conditions and bad health.

"*Few men during their lifetime come near exhausting the resources within them. There are deep wells of strength that are never used.*"[59]

We need to nurture the inside to function effectively in our lives. Emotions such as anger, anxiety, bitterness, frustration, resentment or sadness empty our energy tanks fast. How would you know when it needs filling? We can lose energy if our work or anything we do does not align with our values and purpose in life. If we are unhappy in relationships, careers lack the finances to afford good quality and nutritious food, shelter or a way to make money.

Our energy levels affect our overall wellbeing. The word restore has the word rest in it. Yet, most people keep going and going, eating lunch at the desk or in the car travelling to the next appointment and most often fast processed food.

How often do people want to be refreshed, rejuvenated, revitalised, reinvigorated, or recharged?

These words mean you had the energy, but now it has gone or reduced, and you have to fill up your energy reserve again.

When we constantly spend energy without replacing energy, we become exhausted, depleted and often unable to handle the stressful situations that present throughout life.

Relentless energy demands without renewing, the more dysfunction occurs in organs. When we feel drained, we usually grab a coffee wanting to perk up. However, feeling tired is a warning sign that oxygen and water levels in our bodies are already low or getting low.

If we're finding it hard to focus, concentrate, feel constantly tired, distracted or confused, brain fog and have difficulty making decisions, and feeling exhausted all the time, these are all signs that the oxygen levels in your body are low, and you are most likely already dehydrated too.

Constantly feeling tired could be because our cells need more water to carry out their basic functions like energy production. Signs of chronic dehydration make us fatigued; the brain has trouble focusing and concentrating. The brain triggers a reaction of symptoms giving us lots of warnings that there is a problem.

Often with dehydration by the time you realise you are thirsty you are already dehydrated and that often results in bad headaches or even migraines.

Water is essential and is needed to move contents in the digestive system, constipation occurs, skin becomes dry and flaky, muscle cramps and weakness are clear signs of when the body is dehydrated.

Make sure to drink plenty of filtered water throughout your day.

1. **Oxygenate**. Whenever your energy is low when feeling fatigued, breathe. Follow any breathing techniques you have learned.
2. **Hydration**. Drink water when energy is low and when feeling fatigued. Before you reach for a snack when feeling tired, have a glass of water.
3. **Nutrition.** Lifestyle-related diseases can be reversed through healthy foods. Eating foods comprising the colours of the rainbow offers a variety of vitamins and minerals.

   The higher the plants-based food, the higher the water content to prevent dehydration. Avoid skipping meals unless you are on a program like intermittent fasting. Food is medicine. **Dr. Terry Wahls** reversed Multiple Sclerosis and other neurological conditions through nutrition.[60]

   Dr. David Perlmutter, a Neurologist, says *Alzheimer's can be reversed by food before the disease becomes advanced.*[61]
4. **What is the environment we are living in?**

   We have many toxic substances that we breathe in due to outdoor and indoor pollution that can cause illness. If possible, take the known toxins out of your environment or put in strategies to minimise risks.

Put in good things in your daily environment: items that lift your spirits and create a healthier living and working space including oxygen- producing and air purifying plants for your home or workplace.

5. **Become aware of what is inside you and address what needs attention.**

Pay attention to your thoughts, feelings and emotions. What messages do you get from your body? It is more important not to complain or blame. If you have spent a lot of money on organic food, then complain about the price of food, or the difficulties preparing special meals daily, and feel irritated and angry that you have the health condition, you are undoing all the good you are putting into your body by eating healthier food choices.

Remember your thoughts are pushing out chemicals to match your thoughts. If your emotional state is not happy, your cells are being bathed in depleting and not replenishing hormones. Your frequency will drop and get low, and your organs start vibrating slowly. Think about what you can do, be and have to raise the vibration of all your organs and align your body at a higher frequency.

6. **Build Resilience**

Prepare for stressful situations. Set the tone for your day to be composed. Remember to Breathe!

Use the **Quick Coherence® Technique** when you wake up, driving or before any stressful situation, after a stressful event for 60 seconds and before sleep. Your brain, heart, hormones and organs work in a coordinated way for optimum health. (described in Chapter7)

7. **Become aware of your Circadian Rhythms.**

The Circadian Rhythms influence our metabolism and digestion systems. So, it is helpful for the body if we eat when the sun is up, which is the natural wake-sleep cycle.

Every organ has its own biological clock, but one Master Clock controls all individual clocks. The master clock receives input from the eyes.

When the eyes see light, the master clock tells the cells to be more active and when the light fades to slow down.

The Circadian Rhythm is coordinated with the earth's 24-hour cycle.

Chemicals in the brain adjust hunger, temperature, arousal, awakeness and moods are all dependent and based on our Circadian rhythms.

This really confirms that we are integrated beings, body, mind and spirit.

Sleep

There is so much information in newspapers, magazines and podcasts on sleep, but have you heard of sleep hygiene? These are all the things to embrace for uninterrupted sleep to restore our body to function well in the day and night, and to replenish energy.

Sleep Experts **Don Posner** and **Phillip Gehrman**; both recommend sleep hygiene education. Education on diet, exercise, substance use, and environmental factors (light, noise, temperature) is provided to promote better sleep.

Sleep hygiene includes general sleep facilitation and many recommendations about creating a great sleeping environment.[62]

Suggestions such as: allowing enough time to relax before bedtime, sleeping in a quiet and dark room with few distractions and interruptions.

Good sleep hygiene includes information about the benefits of maintaining a regular sleep schedule.

When we have insomnia, we wake up constantly throughout the night and can't fall back to sleep, more stress hormones get released into our body. If we do not manage our thoughts, foods, actions and emotions during the day, it affects sleep. Bringing your body into coherence will result in better sleep.

Therefore, the **Quick Coherence® Technique** before bed creates a state of ease and calmness.

See a doctor for further investigations for sleep difficulties or sleep apnea to avoid low levels of oxygen.

8. Supplements, Vitamins, Minerals and Herbs

Everyone is different. It will be helpful to see a health practitioner to get a baseline to see if you need supplements. It is better to see what you are deficient in instead of buying off the shelf vitamins that have different levels of vitamins.

If your doctor does not want to give you high doses e.g., Vitamin D which is anti-inflammatory, or high doses of Vitamin C for infections, Vitamin B's Magnesium, Zinc, then collaborate with the doctor by taking research to them from Functional Medical Doctors.

Your doctor will know whether what you take may interact with any medication you are taking or if it impacts on your health conditions.

For example, early in the COVID 19 Pandemic, the general advice or advertisements was for vitamins to boost immunity.

I took my Immunity Boost supplements but noticed Vitiligo becoming more prominent and spreading. Because autoimmune disorders are linked to an overactive immune system, boosting my immune system with vitamins was not helpful.

My immune system needed to be balanced, not boosted so my doctor helped me choose anti-inflammatory supplements and I changed what I ate and monitored when I needed to balance my immunity.

9. **Gut Bacteria**

The digestive system is closely connected with healthy brain function.

New research from the University of Tsukuba in Japan suggests that gut bacteria may also influence standard sleep patterns by helping create critical chemical messengers in the brain, such as serotonin and dopamine which affect the mood.[63] Prebiotics and probiotics are usually taken however check what you are eating, and can you include fermented food?

Check with your health practitioner about gut health who can check for leaky gut, and small intestine bacterial overgrowth.

10. Movement

Movement decreases inflammation and insulin resistance, which is a root cause of many inflammatory diseases, so moving the body is essential.

The type of exercise that you can manage with your breathing, mobility and health condition is important.

For people who are not able to exercise or move, the Mayo Clinic says, *"That vibration machines can help with muscle strength and increase flexibility. The aim is not only to build and maintain muscle mass, but the blood also needs to move through your body to oxygenate your cells."*[64]

Remember, *Motion is lotion.*

***11.* Prayer and Meditation**

Restores energy reserves and increases calmness. Prayer puts the brakes on the stressful response, activating the Parasympathetic System to release replenishing and calming hormones. Breathing deepens, insight, focus and energy increases, improves sleep, concentration and memory, and anxiety quickly decreases.

Self-healing occurs when experiencing oneness with God and meditating on a God who loves and is not punitive.

I would like to invite you:

Take quick 10 breaths when feeling fatigued or any deep breathing technique, you know.

Drink water when feeling tired or hungry after you have had enough food to eat. If you are hungry, don't go immediately for a quick snack. First, try drinking a glass of fresh cool water and get hydrated.

Use a self-regulating technique to control your emotions, thoughts and behaviour: to be calm on the inside, focused, productive and replace with positive energy.

These may be breathing exercises or the **Quick Coherence® Technique.**

The goal or aim is to bring the mind and heart in alignment producing a state of coherence which causes the body to function optimally.

You will become more resilient, feel calmer and you will have the capacity to manage daily stresses.

All these principles will raise your vibration which will increase your wellbeing and empower you to take responsibility for advocating for your health.

Nurturing the inside also means that you honestly and courageously evaluate your life. Take time to reflect on:

Where do I need to change?

Where do I need to grow more?

This is where you will see the health inside you, the many changes you have made and see the improvements in your health.

You will be amazed at the many changes you made in your life, and you will see health improvements and feel fantastic as you nurture the inside world.

Chapter 9

Let Yourself Out

I thought I was free, however over the last ten years as I became aware that my beliefs were limiting and emotions I experienced were depleting and keeping me sick. I became aware that historical, cultural and religious factors hindered my healing from a very early age.

I became excited when I saw that the power of God in me helped me to create a new state of health, calling things into existence that were not. I learned to think about what I wanted, not what I didn't want.

I started imagining and feeling as if it had already happened. I don't know how many times a day I would declare it is finished or it is done. Some days what I looked like did not match my thoughts and the feeling would dip.

I decided that there is credible research and I saw brain scans of people to show that this works. I just kept thanking God as if I had already been healed.

I became aware that my thoughts and emotions were in conflict with my outcomes, so I would have to start again telling myself my brain was rewiring.

I was so excited; I wanted to share what I learned in some of the small informal Christian groups I socialise with.

However, this information was not always received well.

Some people questioned the self-regulating techniques like heart focused breathing that are science validated and used by hundreds of health professionals in North America and the whole Netherlands police services to reduce stress hormones and increase rejuvenation and youthful hormones and said, *"Is it Christian?"*

I was miffed and upset when I heard this. In all my work experience as a Registered Nurse, doing invasive procedures, not one patient ever asked, *"if the nursing intervention I did was Christian?"*

When I told them about Dr. Joe Dispenza's research from meditation and visualisations and how Stage 4 Cancers disappeared in four days of meditation in weeklong conferences, validated by reputable University research,[65] I was told, *"he is not Christian."*

I wondered what we would say to a woman with stage 4 cancer with little children who is healed. Would we say, "*Hallelujah! Her children have their mother, or would we say that the healing mode is invalid.*"

I felt frustrated and disappointed, especially because some of the people would not think of not going to an Emergency Department if they had chest pain or needed surgery for a heart blockage.

I didn't think they would ask the Emergency hospital staff doctors operating and attending nurses, *"if they were Christian."*

I understood that some group members did not accept science because of Charles Darwin's theory of evolution, which is contrary to the belief that humans were created by God.

Evolution and the Big Bang Theory have been superseded. Scientists are now showing that there is an Infinite Intelligence and there is intricate and intelligent design and Creator, although many different names are used such as: The Divine, Higher Power, Infinite Intelligence or Source.

I also understand that it would be hard to accept research findings that show there is no separation with God and that the body, emotions, mind and spirit are separate, especially as the thinking is prevalent in Western thinking.

The small groups I socialise with are united in Christian beliefs of healing and are followers of Jesus Christ, Yet *I felt stifled and restricted.*

Then this quote came to mind:

"You are in prison. You must first realise that you are in prison to get out of prison. If you think you are free, you can't escape."

George Ivanovich Gurdjieff, Spiritual Teacher[66]

I asked myself, *"Am I in prison*? I didn't think I was in prison, and then I heard clearly:

"Let Yourself Out"

It was then that I realised I had been frustrated and disappointed for a long time. These emotions deplete energy and attract thoughts like I am stifled that match the emotions of frustrations.

These emotions make my organs vibrate at a lower speed. These negative emotions cause the stress hormone to be released and circulate for 12 hours in my body. If I didn't change what I thought and felt, I would stay in a prison of chronic illness.

I was reminded the door was not locked and encouraged to let myself out.

Let Yourself Out had more important lessons.

1. **It is a call to repentance.**

   The word repentance comes from the Greek word *Metanoia* which means change your thinking. (Oxford Dictionary)

   Yes, I was judging the people who did not want to hear about my transformation.

   Judging has a low frequency as it comes from pride, anxiety, anger and condemnation. I never even thought of feeling any love towards them. I wanted to be right.

   If I stayed frustrated and disappointed, my genes would stop expressing themselves and lighting themselves up for my optimum health.

2. **It is a call to raise my consciousness.**

   Dr. David R. Hawkins, MD developed a **Map of Consciousness.** (Created to recognise and undo the sources of pain and suffering. Intended to help raise the level of joy that a person can experience due to acknowledging the vibrational level of consciousness).[67]

   The Map of Consciousness has a scale from 1 Hz. up to 1000 Hz. (See page 122).

   You can see my emotions of frustration, which are: feeling less than, anger, disappointment, wanting to be right (pride or ego) have a low frequency.

   Not only does it slow the vibration of my organs down, but you can see, it does not contribute to harmony and joy. See what *my* frequency is against a higher potential.

Frustration/Anger	150
Wanting To Be Right	275
Condemning/Shame	50
Peace	600
Loving	500
Merciful/Accepting	350
Neutral	250
Courage	200

I later learned that Mahatma Gandhi's consciousness level was measured at 700 Hz.

Advanced Enlightenment level is 1000 Hz.

Gandhi became the change he wanted to see in the world.

He was non-violent and brought about India's independence. He was single-minded about his purpose. I realised that I had to be single-minded about *my* purpose.

However, for me to increase my own harmony and joy, I had to give up wanting to be right. Peter Sage reminds students in his Elite Mentorship Forum Program often: **"Do you want to Be Happy or Be Right?"**

I had to raise my level of happiness from the inside out.

Master Transformation

3. **It is a call to Step Up.**

   Letting myself out means speaking up and doing what I am called to do which is to share this message, write this book to assist anyone who needs the information I have to share and to use my gifts, knowledge and tell my story to support people to live freely, fully and feel fantastic.

I have learned to ask questions, so people think for themselves instead of pushing my view on others.

Stepping up is also using wisdom and faith to refer people who need support that I am not trained in or do not have experience e.g. Deliverance ministry, or when people are experiencing very severe complex Post Traumatic Stress conditions.

I also realised it is time to step out or up and write this book that has been in my heart to repair DNA, heal and reclaim health.

"Get out of the park and take a chance! *Act on your vision. The worst thing that can happen is that you gain experience."*[68]

Lance Wallinau

4. **It is a call to move away from the Status Quo.**

The status quo is an enemy of transformation. Waiting to be healed before we can live robs us of joy. Waiting for permission to do things does not change anything in the world. Thinking we are guilty because of our past or the parts we don't want to let anyone know about, doesn't allow us to be accountable for our actions, advocate for ourselves and show up every day.

You and I are needed in the world to calm and bring hope where there is so much chaos, anger, rage, exhaustion and anxiety in the community around us all.

The media keeps saying that a reset is happening in our world during the COVID-19 Pandemic.

No! We do not need a reset; we need refreshing and revival which is brought back to life. This is so needed now with the highest levels of anxiety, division in humanity and chronic disease.

Refreshing and revival will bring us all back to life.

When we step up and out we bring revival, refreshing and live like we are under an open heaven.

I was inspired to do this when I read, **Mystical Union: *Stuff they never told you about the finished work of the Cross.*** John Crowder reminds people that 'We are Revival, and We carry Open Heavens.'[69]

5. **It is a wakeup call to see that the door to the prison is open.**

I started sharing my testimony of transformation outside my usual work setting and personal network. I was amazed at their excitement and enthusiasm to implement strategies and can see their vibrancy increasing.

Here are two examples:

One woman told me that I met in a social setting and that she had a high amount of anxiety. She had so many chronic health conditions which reduced her quality of life. I asked if I could show her how to quickly calm the nervous system with self-regulating techniques. She said, "*I cannot believe how calm I feel, the overwhelm is not there*." This person now catches negative thinking and uses a breathing technique to change her attitude in 60 seconds and is now practising it.

Another person who is not suicidal but wishes death would come due to mobility difficulties and loneliness became animated when he felt better. He became aware of a happy feeling that he didn't experience for a very long time.

It only took a few minutes to interrupt the story that he told everyday which puts out depleting emotions that matches the story he told himself daily waiting for God to take him.

This person now has a new story that releases and replenishes his emotions and energy. By telling himself a new story, it reduces his stress, helps his overall attitude and relieves his chronic pain.

However negative thinking is a habit so practising with him, the **Quick Coherence® Technique** calms his nervous system and turns the lights on his genes on for a higher quality of life. This is an example of healing from the inside out.

When people hear how by shifting their feelings in seconds and that they can release rejuvenating hormones instead of stress hormones, they undo the problem themselves and increase in their joy.

Since stepping up and out, my Pastor has invited me to give a talk and presentation on: **Stress Transformation Education** to the Pastoral team and to the local community during COVID-19. The focus of my presentation is to reduce stress and build resiliency. All my speaking engagements, seminars and presentations have been enthusiastically received to date. I continue to speak and return whenever and wherever I am invited.

I would like to invite you to:

Be your own advocate. Take an hour out a week to learn how to be healthy.

Enjoy meditation and stillness to silence the chatter in your mind.

Meditate and believe that healing has already happened within you, from the inside out.

Write in your **Daily Journal of Awesomeness**.

That is to become aware of when you feel joyful, happy, what were you thinking and do it again to keep this replenishing emotion. Write when you changed your belief and let go of troubling emotions.

Celebrate when you have success or even when an event or person did not trigger you. Write when you noticed symptoms and ask yourself, *"What is the message your body is telling you?*

Pay attention and notice when you: played, laughed and let an offense go by, *"How does your body feel when you keep loving more, laughing often and are feeling grateful for all that is in your life."*

Notice when you feel vibrant and free. Start to pay attention to how often you laugh, are feeling better, and your life is more joyful and peaceful for it. Take note and see all the improvements in your health.

"He will fill your mouth with laughter and your lips with shouts of joy. "

Job 28.1

Conclusion

I finish this book with deep gratitude and appreciation for my late parents, who completed their lives with a new story. Both had tremendous grief and trauma in their childhood and experienced a huge amount of hardship.

I can see their stresses and emotional pain and the effects of living through the Great Depression, World War II, and political and cultural changes in India and Australia that came down through the generations.

Yet they courageously migrated to Australia when they were middle-aged with four children. Within a few years, they bought their first home and went on their first overseas holiday in thirty-two years before my father died.

I too changed my story. I am no longer chronically ill. Understanding that I had to change and live from the inside bringing calmness and co-create a new state of health by believing that I have already been healed.

It has already happened and is done. And so, it is.

"Therefore, I say to you, whatever things you ask when you pray, believe that you receive them, and you will have them."

Mark 11.24

Does that mean there is no tragedy or death? No! However, our bodies are created to self-heal and restore. New research and new science discoveries are confirming and emphasising that love is what heals and repairs DNA. No wonder the Biblical scriptures say we are to love one another.

If you have changed your story or in the process of changing your story to heal and reclaim your health, I would love to hear from you.

There are many modes of healing. However, it is in this Oneness with God where miracles happen.

Living from the inside brings changes in our outer world as well as biological changes throughout our body.

I am honoured to have this opportunity to write this book and that you have read it.

My prayer is that you heal and that you will live freely, fully and feel fantastic.

Footnotes

[1] Louise Hay, "Heal Your Body A-Z. The Mental Causes for Physical Illness and the Way to Overcome" (Carlsbad: Hay House, 2001) 110.

[2] Matthew McDonald, "My People Perish for the Lack of Knowledge" (Thought for the Day Blog, 2009).

[3] David R. Hawkins, "Letting Go. The Pathway of Surrender" (Carlsbad, Hay House, 2012) 24.

[4] Gregg Braden, "Human By Design. From Evolution By Chance to Transformation by Choice" (USA, Penguin Random House, 2007) 81.

[5] Peter Sage, Elite Mentorship Program (Elite Mentorship Forum) (petersage.com).

[6] Joe Dispenza, "Becoming Supernatural. How Common People Are Doing the Uncommon" (USA, Hay House, 2012) 137.

[7] Max Planck, "Quote" (Quote by Max Planck: "[I do not believe] in a personal God, let alone..." (goodreads.com).

[8] Renato Mataso, "Separation and its language in Plato"(PDF) Separation and its language in Plato (researchgate.net),2017.

[9] Jonathon Edwards, "Sinners in the Hands of an Angry God" (Digireads.com Publishing, 2019) 14 –16.

[10] History of the Early Church, "Separation from the World" (www.earlychurch.com).

[11] Baxter Kruger, "God Is For Us"(Jackson, Perichoresis Press,1995) 13.

[12] Timothy Jennings, "How Changing Your View of God Transforms Your Life" (USA, Intervarsity Press,2013) 67-68.

[13] Britannica.com, "Who was Rene Descartes?" (Rene Descartes | Biography, Ideas, Philosophy, 'I Think, Therefore I Am,' & Facts | Britannica).

[14] Fotios S. Fousekis, Aristeidis H. Katsanos, Georgios Kourtis, Maria Saridi, Eleni Albani, Konstantinos H. Katsanos and Dimitrios K. Christodoulou, "Inflammatory Bowel Disease and Patients With Mental Disorders: What Do We Know?" (J Clin Med Res, 2021 Sep,13(9) 466–473.

[15] Jeffrey, K. Griffith, "Vitamin Deficiencies" (in Hunter Tropical Medicine and Emerging Infection Disease, 9th Edition, 2013).

[16] HeartMath Institute, "The Physiology of Coherence and Optimum Functioning" (The Resilience Program, www.heartmath.org 2014) 12-1.

[17] Genomes and Precision Health, "What is Epigenetics?" (Centre for Disease Control, www.cdc.gov).

[18] Mandana Molana "(Rumi) Poems in Farsi and English" (www.Nikmood.com, 2021).

[19] Neville Goddard, "Feeling is the Secret" (https//www.feelingisthe secret.org).

[20] Gregg Braden, "Human By Design, From Evolution By Chance to Transformation by Choice' (USA, Penguin Random House, 2007) Inspirit Wellness,(Gregg Braden - Quantum Healing of Tumour thru the Power of Thought & Feeling - YouTube).

[21] Joe Dispenza, "Breaking the Habit of Being Yourself. How to lose Your Mind and Create a New one" (USA, Hay House, 2012).

[22] Albert Einstein "Imagination Quotes" (Imagination Quotes (3353 quotes) (goodreads.com).

[23] Stephen Covey, "The 7 Habits of Highly Effective People" (USA, Simon & Schuster, 2013).

[24] Joe Dispenza Face Book Page 2020 & "Breaking the Habit of Being Yourself. How to Lose Your Mind and Create a New One" (USA, Hay House, 2012).

[25] Valerie Sabater, "Imagination"(Imagination|Psychology Today, 2021).

[26] Shana Schutte, "The Power of God Given Imagination"(The Power of God-given Imagination - Focus on the Family,2008).

[27] Joe Dispenza, "Breaking the Habit of Being Yourself. How to lose Your Mind and Create a New one" (USA, Hay House, 2012).

[28] Donald Hebb, "How Neurons that Fire Together Wire Together" (www.NeuroscienceNews.com, 2021).

[29] CS Lewis, "Mere Christianity Quotes" www.goodreads.com).

[30] Bruce Lipton, "The Biology of Belief, Unleashing the Power of Consciousness, Matter & Miracles" (USA, Hay House, 2008)129.

[31] Christopher Maher, Adrian Traeger, Abdel Shaheed, Christina Abdel Shaheed and Mary O'Keeffe, "Placebos in Clinical Care, A Suggestion Beyond Evidence" (The Medical Journal of Australia, 2012).

[32] Bruce Lipton, "The Biology of Belief, Unleashing the Power of Consciousness, Matter & Miracles" (USA, Hay House, 2008)136.

[33] Henry Ford "Quote" (www.goodreads.com).

[34] Joe; Friedman, "The Benefits of Suffering and the Cost of Wellbeing: Secondary Gains and Losses and Stress Reduction Information" (The Benefits Of Suffering And The Costs Of Well Being: Secondary Gains And Losses - Mental Help).

[35] Herbert Goldenberg & Irene Goldenberg, "Family Therapy. An Overview (Thompson Brooks/Cole, USA, 2008) 4,195.

[36] Ken Blue, "Authority To Heal" (USA, IVP Books, 2009).

[37] HeartMath Institute, "Raising Our Vibrations Through Compassion and Unconditional Love"(HeartMath Institute, (www.heartmath.org 2017).

[38] Bruce Lipton, "The Biology of Belief. Unleashing the Power of Consciousness, Matter & Miracles" (Australia, Hay House, 2008) 137-138.

[39] HeartMath Institute, "You Can Change Your DNA" (https://www.heartmath.org/articles-of-the-heart/personal-development/you-can-change-your-dna/ 2011).

[40] Louise Hay, "Affirmations to Heal Your Body." (www.loveyourbody.com).

[41] Masaru Emoto, "Water Crystal Experiments" (www.Hexagonalwater.com).

[42] Mahatma Gandhi "Quote": "Your beliefs become your thoughts, Your though..." (goodreads.com).

[43] HeartMath Institute, The Resilience Advantage™ A HeartMath Certified Trainer Program (www.heartmath.com) 2014.

[44] The National Foundation for Cancer Research, "Shame-Cancer" (https://www.nfcr.org/blog/shame-cancer/ 2021).

[45] Joe Dispenza, Becoming Supernatural. How Common People Are Doing the Uncommon (Australia, Hay House, 2017).

[46] HeartMath Institute, Raising Our Vibrations Through Compassion and Unconditional Love (www.heartmath.org, 2017).

[47] David R. Hawkins, Letting Go, The Pathway of Surrender (USA, Hay House, 2013) 229.

[48] Mayo Clinic, Letting Go of Grudges and Bitterness (www.mayoclinic.org).

[49] Glenn Fox, What Can the Brain Reveal About Gratitude? (https://www.goodreads.com/work/quotes/801500-mere-christianity).

[50] Norman Cousins, Anatomy of an Illness Video (Online Laughter University, 1983).

[51] Roy T. Bennett, "Quote" (www.goodreads.com).

[52] Harvard University, Centre for the Developing Child. Epigenetics and Child Development: "How Children's Experiences Affect Their Genes" (Harvard University).

[53] Jean-Pierre Barral, Understanding the Messages of Your Body (Berkley, North Atlantic Books, 2007) 30

[54] Martez Schembri, "From Stress to Bliss. A Journey from Post-Traumatic Stress to Post-Traumatic Growth" (Ontario, BlackCard Publishing, 2019).

[55] Bessel Van Der Kolk, The Body Keeps The Score. Mind, Brain and Body in the Transformation of Trauma UK, Penguin Random House UK 2015).

[56] Joe Dispenza, "Breaking the Habit of Being Yourself. How to lose Your Mind and Create a New one" (USA, Hay House, 2012).

[57] Peter Sage, Elite Mentorship Program (Elite Mentorship Forum) (petersage.com).

[58] HeartMath Institute. "The Quick Coherence® Technique" (www.HeartMath.org).

[59] Richard E. Byrd, Alone: The Classic Polar Adventure (USA, Shearwater Brooks (Island Press, 1st Edition, 2003) (www.goodreads.com).

[60] Terry Wahl, "Research Backed Strategies to Managing Multiple Sclerosis and other Autoimmune Diseases" (www.terrywahl.com).

[61] Dr. David Perlmutter, "Reversing Alzheimer's Disease, Yes Alzheimer's Can be Reversed" (https://www.drperlmutter.com/).

[62] Don Posner and Phillip Gehrman, Sleep Hygiene, Behaviour for Sleep Disorders (Mental Health Profession, 2011) 36-43.

[63] Jennifer Huizen, How Gut Microbes Contribute to Good Sleep (MedicalNewstoday.com, 2020).

[64] Edward R. Laskowski, "Is whole body vibration a good way to lose weight and improve fitness?" (Mayoclinic.org)

[65] Joe Dispenza, "Becoming Supernatural: How Common People Are Doing the Uncommon" (USA, Hay House, 2012).

[66] George Ivanovich Gurdjieff Quote by G.I. Gurdjieff: "You are in prison. If you wish to get out of pr..." (goodreads.com)

[67] David, R. Hawkins, "Map of Consciousness, Letting go, The Pathway to Surrender" (USA, Hay House 2012) 336.

[68] Lance Wallinau, Quote by Lance Wallinau (www.lancewallinau.com).

[69] John Crowder, "Mystical Union: Stuff they Never told You About the Finished Work of the Cross" (Sons of Thunder Ministries & Publications, 2010).

Bibliography

1. Barral, Jean-Pierre: *Understanding the Messages of Your Body,* North Atlantic Books 2007.
2. Braden, Gregg: *Human By Design. From Evolution By Choice,* Penguin Random House. USA 2007.
3. Blue, Ken, *Authority to Heal*, IVP Books. USA, 2009.
4. Britannica.com, "Who was Rene Descartes?"
5. Byrd, Richard, E. Alone. The Classic Polar Adventure (USA, Shearwater Brooks (Island Press, 1st Edition, 2003 (www.goodreads.com) .
6. Centre for Disease Control, *Genomes and Precision Health*. "What is Epigenetics?" (Centre for Disease Control, www.cdc.gov).
7. Cousins, Norman: Anatomy of an Illness Video (Online Laughter University).
8. Covey, Stephen R., *The 7 Habits of Highly Effective People*, Simon & Schuster, USA, 2013.
9. Crowder, John, Mystical *Union: Stuff They Never Told You About The Finished Work of the Cross,* Sons of Thunder Ministries & Publications, 2010.
10. Dispenza, Joe, Becoming Supernatural. How Common People Are Doing the Uncommon, Hay House, USA, 2017.
11. Dispenza, Joe, *Breaking the Habit of Being Yourself. How To Lose Your Mind and Create A New One*, Hay House, USA, 2012.
12. Dispenza, Joe, *You Are The Placebo*. Encephalon. LLC 2014.
13. Emoto, Masaru: *Water crystal experiments,* www.Hexagonal Water.com

14. Edwards, Jonathon: *Sinners in the Hands of an Angry God,* Digireads.com Publishing, 2019.

15. Fousekis FS, Katsanos AH, Kourtis G, Saridi M, Albani E, Katsanos KH, Christodoulou DK.: "Inflammatory Bowel Disease and Patients with Mental Disorders: What Do We Know?" (J Clin Med Res, 2021 Sep,13(9) 466–473).

16. Fox, Glenn: *What can the brain reveal about gratitude?* Greater Good Science Centre, 2017.

17. Friedman, Joe: *"The Benefits of Suffering and the Cost of Wellbeing: Secondary Gains and Losses and Stress Reduction Information"* (https://www.mentalhelp.net/blogs/the-benefits-of-suffering-and-the-costs-of-well-being-secondary-gains-and-losses/).

18. Griffith, Jeffrey, K: *Vitamin Deficiencies* (in Hunter Tropical Medicine and Emerging Infection Disease, 9th Edition, 2013.

19 Goddard, Neville: *Feeling is the Secret* (https//www.feelingisthe secret.org),

20 Goldenberg, Herbert & Goldenberg, Irene: *Family Therapy, An Overview, Thomson Brooks Coles, USA, 2008.*

21 Harvard University, Centre for the Developing Child. Epigenetics and Child Development: *How Children's Experiences Affect their Genes* (Harvard University).

22 Hay, Louise: *Heal Your Body, A-Z. The Mental Causes for Physical Illness and the Way to Overcome*, Carlsbad, Hay House, 2001.

23 Hay, Louise: *Affirmations to Heal Your Body,* www.louisehay.com

24 HeartMath: *Raising our vibrations through compassion and unconditional love.* HeartMath.org, 2017.

25 HeartMath Institute: "The Quick Coherence® Technique" (HeartMath.org).

26 HeartMath Institute: “The Physiology of Coherence and Optimum Functioning” (The Resilience Program, www.heartmath.org 2014) 12-1.

27 HeartMath: *You Can Change Your DNA*, HearthMath.org, 2011.

28 Hebb, Donald: *Neurons that Fire Together Wire Together*, The 24 Information Philosopher, 2017.

29 History of the Early Church: *Separation from the World*, Earlychurch.com

30 Huizen, Jennifer: *How Gut Microbes Contribute to Good Sleep*, MedicalNewstoday.com, 2020).

31 Jennings, Timothy: *How Changing Your View of God Transforms Your Life.* InterVarsity Press. USA, 2013.

32 Kruger, C. Baxter: *God Is For Us*, Perichoresis Press, USA, 1999.

33 Laskowski, Edward, R*: Is whole body vibration a good way to lose weight and improve fitness?(*www.Mayoclinic.com).

34 Lipton, Bruce: *The Biology of Belief. Unleashing the Power of Consciousness*, Matter & Miracles, Hay House, USA, 2008.

35 Masato, Renato: *Separation and its language in Plato,* Researchgate.net, 2017.

36 Mayo Clinic Staff**:** *Forgiveness: Letting Go of Grudges and Bitterness, Mayo* clinic.

37 Mandana, *Molena: (Rumi) written in Farsi and English,* www.Nikmood.com, 2021.

38 Maher, Christopher; Traeger, Adrian: Abdel Shaheed, Christina Abdel Shaheed and O'Keeffe, Mary: *Placebos in clinical care, a suggestion beyond the evidence,* The Medical Journal of Australia (mja.com.au), 2021.

39 McCraty, Rollin, Science of the Heart. *Exploring the Role of the Heart in Human Performance. An Overview of Research:* HeartMath Institute, Volume 2, 2015.

40 McDonald, Matthew: *My People Perish for the Lack of Knowledge*. Thought for Today, Blog 2009.

41 Sage, Peter: Elite Mentorship Program, (www.petersage.com).

42 One God Worship: *How Plato Influenced Our View* of God, www.One God Worship.com

43 Perlmutter, Dr. David: *Reversing Alzheimer's Disease, Yes Alzheimer's Can be Reversed (*https://www.drperlmutter.com/)

44 Posner, D, Gehrman P: *Sleep Hygiene, Behaviour for Sleep Disorders*, Mental Health Profession, 2011.

45 Ryrie, Charles. New International Version Bible, Biblica, 1973.

46 Sabater, Valerie: *Imagination* (Psychology Today.com 2021).

47 Schembri, Martez, "From Stress to Bliss. A Journey from Post-Traumatic Stress to Post-Traumatic Growth" Ontario, BlackCard Publishing, 2019.

48 Schutte, Shana: *The Power of God Given Imagination,* Focus on the Family, 2008.

49 The National Foundation for Cancer Research: *Shame-Cancer*,2021.

50 Van Der Kolk, Bessel: *The Body Keeps the Score.* Mind, *Brain and Body in the Transformation of Trauma*, Penguin Psychology. USA, 2015.

51 Wahl, Terry: *Research Backed Strategies to Managing Multiple Sclerosis and other Autoimmune Diseases* (https://terrywahls.com/).

Resources

Everything You Need To Know About Supplements, A Functional Medicine Perspective. An Evidence based review.

HeartMath Institute Free Videos, Information on trauma programs and resilience programs for children.

Letting Go ~ The Sedona Method. www.sedonamethod.com

David R. Hawkins, Map Of Consciousness (Map taken from Letting Go ~ The Pathway of Surrender by Dr. David R. Hawkins)

Veterans and First Responders Resources for Trauma www.heartmath.org

Veterans and Families in Australia Help Line: 1800 011 046

The Map of Consciousness

God-view	Life-View	Level		Log	Emotion	Process
Self	Is	Enlightenment	↑	700-1000	Ineffable	Pure consciousness
All-Being	Perfect	Peace	↑	600	Bliss	Illumination
One	Complete	Joy	↑	540	Serenity	Transfiguration
Loving	Benign	Love	↑	500	Reverence	Revelation
Wise	Meaningful	Reason	↑	400	Understanding	Abstraction
Merciful	Harmonious	Acceptance	↑	350	Forgiveness	Transcendence
Inspiring	Hopeful	Willingness	↑	310	Optimism	Intention
Enabling	Satisfactory	Neutrality	↑	250	Trust	Release
Permitting	Feasible	Courage	↕	200	Affirmation	Empowerment
Indifferent	Demanding	Pride	↓	175	Scorn	Inflation
Vengeful	Antagonistic	Anger	↓	150	Hate	Aggression
Denying	Disappointing	Desire	↓	125	Craving	Enslavement
Punitive	Frightening	Fear	↓	100	Anxiety	Withdrawal
Disdainful	Tragic	Grief	↓	75	Regret	Despondency
Condemning	Hopeless	Apathy	↓	50	Despair	Abdication
Vindictive	Evil	Guilt	↓	30	Blame	Destruction
Despising	Miserable	Shame	↓	20	Humiliation	Elimination

The Map of Consciousness courtesy of David R. Hawkins, **Letting Go.** The Pathway of Surrender (USA Hay House 2013).

About the Author

Ruth Littler was born in South India and migrated to Australia as a child with her family. Ruth completed her Bachelor of Nursing and Master of Social Science (Counselling) and trained as a Health Coach, Elite Mentorship and HeartMath® Certified Trainer and is a Registered Nurse. In 2021, she founded 360 Wellbeing, a Coaching Consulting Service that focuses on Stress Transformation, Resilience and Reclaiming Health.

Ruth experienced chronic illness for more than ten (10) years. Sick of being sick, Ruth looked for answers that were true to a loving and healing God. She also researched Epigenetics, New Biology, Nutrition, Resilience, and Biblical scriptures and applied them to heal and reclaim her health.

Ruth's mission is to empower people to transform from the inside out, live freely, fully and feel fantastic.

Ruth is married with two adult children and lives in Perth, Western Australia.

You can connect with Ruth Littler through www.ruthlittler.com.au

Ingram Content Group UK Ltd.
Milton Keynes UK
UKHW021049120323
418359UK00011B/121